Hirsch

SCIENCE WORKSHOP SERIES

Physical Science

Annotated Teacher's Edition

CHEMICAL CHANGES

Seymour Rosen

GLOBE FEARON

Pearson Learning Group

D1501181

CONTENTS

Introduction to the Series T-1

    Overview T-1

    Using the Books T-1

    Objectives T-1

Skills Matrix T-2

Verbal Skills T-3

Language Diverse Populations T-3

Concept Development T-3

Safety in the Science Laboratory T-4

Using the Teacher's Edition T-4

Answer Key for Review Test T-4

Review Test T-5–T-6

Lesson Teaching Strategies T-7–T-14

ISBN 0-130-23380-3
Printed in the United States of America
3 4 5 6 7 8 9   06 05 04 03 02

1-800-321-3106
www.pearsonlearning.com

INTRODUCTION TO THE SERIES

Overview

The *Science Workshop Series* consists of 12 softbound workbooks that provide a basic secondary-school science program for students achieving below grade level. General competency in the areas of biology, earth science, chemistry, and physical science is stressed. The series is designed so that the books may be used sequentially within or across each of these science areas.

Each workbook consists of approximately 30 lessons. Each lesson opens with a manageable amount of text for students to read. The succeeding pages contain exercises, many of which include photographs or drawings. The illustrations provide students with answers to simple questions. Phonetic spellings and simple definitions for scientific terms are also included to aid in the assimilation of new words.

The question material is varied and plentiful. Exercises such as *Completing Sentences, Matching,* and *True or False* are used to reinforce material covered in the lesson. An open-ended *Reaching Out* question often completes the lesson with a slightly more challenging, yet answerable question.

Easy-to-do laboratory experiments are also included in some lessons. Not isolated, the experiments are part of the development of concepts. They are practical experiments, which require only easily obtainable, inexpensive materials.

Numerous illustrations and photographs play an important role in the development of concepts as well. The functional art enhances students' understanding and relates scientific concepts to students' daily lives.

The workbook format meets the needs of the reluctant student. The student is given a recognizable format, short lessons, and questions that are not overwhelming. The student can handle the stepwise sequence of question material in each lesson with confidence.

The series meets the needs of teachers as well. The workbooks can either be used for an entire class simultaneously, or since the lessons are self-contained, the books can be used on an individual basis for remedial purposes. This works well because the tone of each book is informal; a direct dialogue is established between the book and the student.

Using the Books

Although each lesson's reading selection may be read as part of a homework assignment, it will prove most effective if it is read during class time. This allows for an introduction to a new topic and a possible discussion. Teacher demonstrations that help to reinforce the ideas stressed in the reading should also be done during class time.

The developmental question material that follows the reading can serve as an ideal follow-up to do in class. The exercises such as *Completing Sentences, True or False* or *Matching* might be assigned for homework or used as a short quiz. The *Reaching Out* question might also be assigned for homework or completed in class to end a topic with a discussion.

Objectives

The aim of the *Science Workshop Series* is to increase the student's level of competency in two areas: *Science Skills* and *Verbal Skills*. The comprehensive skills matrix on page T-2 highlights the science skills that are used in each lesson.

SKILLS MATRIX

Lesson	Identifying	Classifying	Observing	Measuring	Inferring	Interpreting	Predicting	Modeling	Experimenting	Organizing	Analyzing	Understanding Direct and Indirect Relationships	Inductive Reasoning	Deductive Reasoning
1	●													●
2	●		●	●	●				●		●		●	●
3	●		●				●				●			●
4	●		●			●							●	●
5	●		●		●						●			●
6	●		●											●
7					●						●			
8	●				●		●				●			●
9		●								●	●			●
10		●	●		●	●	●			●	●	●		●
11	●	●	●									●		
12		●	●						●	●		●		
13	●		●	●			●				●	●		●
14	●	●	●		●	●			●					●
15	●	●	●		●		●			●	●	●		●
16	●	●	●		●	●	●			●	●			●
17	●	●	●				●	●	●	●	●			●
18	●		●		●	●	●				●		●	●
19		●	●		●		●			●	●	●	●	
20			●	●	●	●	●	●	●	●	●	●		
21	●		●	●			●	●	●	●	●		●	
22	●		●		●	●	●					●	●	
23	●		●		●		●					●		
24	●		●		●	●	●					●		●
25	●	●	●							●		●		●
26	●	●				●	●			●				
27	●	●			●					●	●	●		
28	●	●					●			●				
29						●				●		●		●
30	●	●									●			●
31	●			●	●				●		●	●		●
32	●	●					●			●	●			●
33	●	●	●							●	●			●
34	●	●				●		●		●	●			●
35														

VERBAL SKILLS

An important objective of the *Science Workshop Series* is to give all students—even those with reading difficulties—a certain degree of science literacy. Reading science materials is often more difficult for poor readers because of its special vocabulary. Taking this into account, each new word is introduced, defined, used in context, and repeated in order to increase its familiarity. The development of the vocabulary word **mixture** is traced below to illustrate the usage of science words in the text.

1. The word **mixture** is first defined in Lesson 12 on page 73.
2. Students distinguish between mixtures and compounds on page 74.
3. The *True or False* exercise on page 76 requires students to review the definition of **mixture**.
4. The experiments on page 76 and 77 work with common mixtures.
5. The word is reintroduced and used throughout Lessons 13–21, which deal with mixtures and solutions.

This stepwise development allows students to gradually increase their working science vocabulary.

Other techniques used to familiarize students with a specialized vocabulary are less formal and allow the student to have fun while reinforcing what has been learned.

- A *Word Search* appears on page 208.
- A *Word Scramble* appears on page 6.

LANGUAGE DIVERSE POPULATIONS

Students with limited English proficiency may encounter difficulties with the core material as well as the language. Teachers of these students need to use ample repetition, simple explanations of key concepts, and many concrete examples from the students' world. Relying on information students already possess helps students gain confidence and establishes a positive learning environment.

To help LDP students with language development, it is important to maintain an open dialogue between the students and the teacher. Encourage student participation. Have students submit written and oral reports. After students read a section of the text, have them explain it in their own words. These strategies will help the teacher be aware of problem areas.

CONCEPT DEVELOPMENT

In each book the lessons are arranged in such a way as to provide a logical sequence that students can easily follow. Let us trace the development of one concept from the workbook: *Two or more substances combine chemically to form a compound.*

Lesson 8 introduces students to the concept of a compound. In Lesson 12, the differences between compounds and mixtures are explained. The types of compounds formed when acids and bases are formed is discussed in Lesson 24. Lesson 30 introduces the equations used to describe the formations of compounds. Finally, Lessons 32, 33, 34, and 35 discuss the types of reactions compounds may take part in.

SAFETY IN THE SCIENCE LABORATORY

Many of the lessons in the books of the *Science Workshop Series* include easy-to-do laboratory experiments. In order to have a safe laboratory environment, there are certain rules and procedures that must be followed. It is the responsibility of every science teacher to explain safety rules and procedures to students and to make sure that students adhere to these safety rules.

To help students develop an awareness of safety in the science laboratory, a list of Safety Symbols and Warnings is included at the end of this workshop.

USING THE TEACHER'S EDITION

The Teacher's Edition of *Physical Science: Chemical Changes* has on-page annotations for all questions, exercises, charts, tables, and so on. It also includes front matter with teaching suggestions for each lesson in the book. Every lesson begins with questions to motivate the lesson. The motivational questions relate to the lesson opener pictures and provide a springboard for discussion of the lesson's science concepts. Following the *Motivation* are a variety of teaching strategies. Suggestions for *Class Activities, Demonstrations, Extensions, Reinforcements,* and *Cooperative/ Collaborative Learning* opportunities are given.

The teacher's edition also includes a two-page test, which includes at least one question from each lesson in the book. The text can be photocopied and distributed to students. It begins on the next page. The test's Answer Key is found below.

ANSWER KEY FOR REVIEW TEST

Multiple Choice

1. c   **2.** d   **3.** b   **4.** c   **5.** d   **6.** c   **7.** d   **8.** d   **9.** a   **10.** a

Fill In The Blank

1. expand   **2.** Fahrenheit, Celsius   **3.** filtration   **4.** solute, solvent   **5.** emulsions
6. electrons   **7.** polyatomic ion   **8.** ions   **9.** oxidation   **10.** reduction

True Or False

1. false   **2.** true   **3.** true   **4.** false   **5.** false   **6.** true   **7.** true   **8.** false   **9.** false
10. true

Matching

1. b   **2.** a   **3.** f   **4.** e   **5.** g   **6.** h   **7.** c   **8.** j   **9.** i   **10.** d

Name _____ Class _____ Date _____

MULTIPLE CHOICE

In the space provided, write the letter of the word or words that best complete each statement.

_____ 1. The mass of one molecule of a compound is called its
a) formula weight. b) atomic weight. c) formula mass. d) atomic mass.

_____ 2. Elements combining to form a compound is an example of a
a) replacement reaction. b) decomposition reaction. c) physical change.
d) synthesis reaction.

_____ 3. The smallest part of a compound is
a) an element or mixture. b) a molecule or formula unit.
c) an atom or ion. d) a metal or nonmetal.

_____ 4. A mixture in which one substance is evenly mixed with another substance is
called a
a) solvent. b) solute. c) solution. d) crystal.

_____ 5. A solution that contains all the solute it can hold is said to be
a) dilute. b) concentrated. c) unsaturated. d) saturated.

_____ 6. The process by which a liquid changes to a gas is called
a) distillation. b) condensation. c) evaporation. d) sedimentation.

_____ 7. The formula for water is
a) HO. b) H_2O_2. c) HO_2. d) H_2O.

_____ 8. Which of the following pH measures shows a strong acid?
a) pH 14. b) pH 10. c) pH 7. d) pH 2.

_____ 9. Iron filings and powdered sulfur in a beaker is
a) a mixture. b) a compound. c) a solution. d) an emulsion.

_____ 10. Soapy water is
a) a base. b) an acid. c) neutral. d) solute.

FILL IN THE BLANK

Complete each statement using a term from the list below. Write your answers in the spaces provided.

expand	Fahrenheit	electrons	polyatomic ion
emulsions	Celsius	solute	oxidation
filtration	ions	solvent	reduction

1. Heat makes matter _____ .

2. Temperatures can be measured in degrees _____ or _____ .

3. The method of separating a suspension by trapping particles is _____ .

4. The two parts of a solution are the _____ and _____ .

5. Liquid solutions are called _____ .

6. Atoms in molecules share _____ .

7. A group of atoms that behave like a single atom is called a _____ .

8. Atoms that have a charge are _____ .

9. _____ takes place when oxygen combines with another substance.

10. _____ takes place when oxygen separates from another substance.

TRUE OR FALSE

In the space provided, write "true" if the sentence is true. Write "false" if the sentence is false.

_____ 1. Compounds link up to make elements.

_____ 2. A magnet can be used to separate some mixtures.

_____ 3. The liquid part of a solution is the solvent.

_____ 4. A pot of boiling water has a higher temperature than a lit match.

_____ 5. Polyvalent elements have only one oxidation number.

_____ 6. Stirring makes solutes dissolve faster.

_____ 7. Adding solutes to water makes the water more difficult to freeze.

_____ 8. An acid is neutral.

_____ 9. In a chemical reaction, matter is destroyed.

_____ 10. In a double replacement reaction, two compounds react to form two different compounds.

MATCHING

Match each term in Column A with its description in Column B. Write the correct letter in the space provided.

	Column A		Column B
_____	1. heat	a)	how heat moves through solids
_____	2. conduction	b)	causes particles to vibrate faster
_____	3. physical change	c)	a chemical reaction takes place
_____	4. miscible	d)	how heat moves through empty space
_____	5. convection	e)	mixable
_____	6. oxidation numbers	f)	no new substances are formed
_____	7. chemical change	g)	how heat moves through liquids and gases
_____	8. chemical equation	h)	the number of electrons an atom can lend or borrow
_____	9. synthesis reaction	i)	opposite of a decomposition reaction
_____	10. radiation	j)	describes a chemical reaction

LESSON TEACHING STRATEGIES

LESSON 1
What is heat? (pp. 1–6)

Motivation   Refer students to the lesson opener picture on page 1 and ask the following questions:

1. Which picture shows a hot place?

2. Which picture shows a cold place?

Discussion   Have students name the five main forms of energy. Then discuss heat as a form of energy. Develop the concept that heat energy is related to the motion of molecules.

Demonstration   Pour equal amounts of cold water and hot water into separate beakers. Add a drop of food coloring to each beaker. Tell students to note in which beaker the food coloring spreads faster. Point out that the particles of water are constantly moving, so the food coloring is being spread throughout the water. The particles in the hot water are moving faster, causing the food coloring in hot water to spread out faster.

Class Activity   Have students rub their hands together to show that friction produces heat.

LESSON 2
How does heat change the size of matter? (pp. 7–14)

Motivation   Refer students to the lesson opener picture on page 7 and ask the following questions:

1. Which bottle is being heated?

2. In which picture would the liquid take up more space?

Laboratory Experiment   How do heat and cold change the size of a solid?

Materials   brass ring, brass ball that "just" fits through the ring, Bunsen burner, cold water

Procedure   This experiment will take about 15 minutes. Students may work together in small groups or the experiment may be done as a demonstration. Caution students to be careful when heating the brass ball.

Laboratory Experiment   How do heat and cold change the size of a liquid?

Materials   Pyrex bottle, cold colored water, one-hole stopper with glass tube, warm water, large beaker

Advance Preparation   Refrigerate water for use in the Pyrex bottle. Adding food coloring to

the cold water is not necessary, but will make it easier for the students. Heat water for use in the large beaker.

Procedure   This experiment will take about 15 minutes. Students may work together in small groups or the experiment may be done as a demonstration. Tell students to make sure that the water level in the glass tube rises above the stopper.

Laboratory Experiment   How do heat and cold change the size of a gas?

Materials   Pyrex bottles, cold colored water, one-holed stopper, glass tube with bulb

Advance Preparation   Refrigerate water for use in the Pyrex bottle. Adding food coloring to the cold water is not necessary, but will make it easier for the students.

Procedure   This experiment will take about 15 minutes. Students may work together in small groups or the experiment may be done as a demonstration. Tell students to make sure that the water level in the glass tube rises into the bulb. Caution students not to squeeze the bulbed end of the glass tube or they may break it.

Demonstration   To show students the thermal expansion of gases, stretch a balloon over the mouth of a flask. Gently heat the flask. Students will observe that the balloon gets larger. Point out that the balloon gets larger as heated air expands.

Demonstration   To show that water expands when it freezes, fill a container with water to the very top. Cover the container and place it in a freezer. Have the students note that when the water froze, it cracked the container.

LESSON 3
How does heat move through solids? (pp. 15–20)

Motivation   Refer students to the lesson opener picture on page 15 and ask the following questions:

1. Why are frying pans made of metals?

2. What happens to a spoon if you leave it in a hot cup of tea?

Discussion   Hold up a metal cooking pot in front of the classroom and discuss why metals are used as cooking utensils. Point out that metals are good conductors of heat. Define a conductor as a substance that allows heat to move through it easily. Then compare conductors and insulators.

Demonstration To show students that wood and wax are two examples of insulators, hold up a lighted candle and a lighted match. Ask students why your fingers are not burned.

LESSON 4
How does heat move through liquids and gases? (pp. 21–26)

Motivation Refer students to the lesson opener picture on page 21 and ask the following questions:

1. What happens to the smoke that comes out of a chimney?

2. How is the air in the lower right picture circulating?

Reinforcement Be sure that students understand that convection currents are due to differences in density. Point out that warm air is less dense than cold air because the particles in warm air are farther apart.

Demonstration Show that the heat from a candle is carried upward by a convection current. A strip of paper held close to the side of the candle will not catch fire. Hold it above and it quickly bursts into flame. The heat is carried to the paper above by a convection current of hot gases.

LESSON 5
How does heat move through empty space? (pp. 27–32)

Motivation Refer students to the lesson opener picture on page 27 and ask the following questions:

1. What is there between the Sun and Earth?

2. What do the Sun and a radiator have in common?

Class Activity Allow students to examine a radiometer. Show how it operates in sunlight, but stops when the sunlight is blocked. Point out that heat and light energy from the sun cause the movement of the radiometer.

LESSON 6
What is the difference between heat and temperature? (pp. 33–38)

Motivation Refer students to the lesson opener picture on page 33 and ask the following questions:

1. Which is hotter, a bowl of soup or a candle flame?

2. What device is shown in the upper left figure?

Reinforcement Before beginning this lesson, remind students that temperature is a measure of how much heat energy an object contains and that temperature is measured with a thermometer.

Demonstration To show students the difference between heat and temperature, fill two beakers, one large and one small, with hot water. Use a thermometer to make sure the temperature of the water is the same in each beaker. Then place several ice cubes into each beaker. Students will observe that when the ice cubes melt, the temperature change is less in the large beaker than in the small beaker. Point out that there was less change in temperature in the large beaker because the large beaker has more heat energy.

LESSON 7
How does a thermometer work? (pp. 39–44)

Motivation Refer students to the lesson opener picture on page 39 and ask the following questions:

1. What are the three items pictured?

2. What do these items measure?

Class Activity Tell students to record the daily high and low temperatures in degrees Celsius for the next week. Point out that while the United States uses the Fahrenheit scale, most countries use the Celsius scale. In the U.S., temperature readings usually are given in both degrees Fahrenheit and degrees Celsius.

Extension Have students find out the equations used to convert from Fahrenheit to Celsius and Celsius to Fahrenheit. Have students practice converting from one temperature scale to another.

LESSON 8
What are compounds? (pp. 45–50)

Motivation Refer students to the lesson opener picture on page 45 and ask the following questions:

1. What four elements are shown?

2. What elements do you think join to form a molecule of water? What elements make up table salt?

Demonstration Heat some sugar in a test tube. Have the students note that the sugar melts and then only a black solid remains. Point out that the black solid is carbon. Carbon is left in the test tube when hydrogen and oxygen gas are released into the air. Elicit from students that carbon, hydrogen, and oxygen are the three elements that combine to form sugar. Point out that sugar is a compound. Use this example to illustrate how the properties of a compound are very different from the properties of the elements that make it up.

Class Activity   Divide the class into small groups to make models of the molecules shown in the lesson. Tell students to cut out different colored circles to represent atoms and to join the atoms together to make molecules. Alternatively, students may use modeling clay to make their models.

LESSON 9
What is a chemical formula? (pp. 51–56)

Motivation   Refer students to the lesson opener picture on page 51 and ask the following questions:

1. What is the chemical symbol for sodium? for chlorine? for hydrogen? for oxygen?

2. How many atoms of sodium do you think are in each molecule of table salt? How many atoms of hydrogen are in each molecule of water?

Reinforcement   Give students practice reading chemical formulas. Write the formulas for a variety of compounds on the chalkboard. Ask students what elements make up each compound. Be sure students understand that the subscript 1 is never written in a chemical formula.

Reinforcement   Have students look up the meaning of the prefix "sub-" in a dictionary, to help them understand the placement of a subscript in a chemical formula.

LESSON 10
How do elements form compounds ? (pp. 57–64)

Motivation   Refer students to the lesson opener picture on page 57 and ask the following questions:

1. What three types of particles make up both a sodium atom and a chlorine atom? How many electrons does a sodium atom have? How many electrons does a chlorine atom have?

2. How do you think sodium and chlorine atoms combine to form table salt?

Reinforcement   Review the structure of an atom before discussing bonds. Ask students what atoms are made of. Then ask what is the charge of each particle. Remind students that electrons orbit the nucleus in shells.

LESSON 11
What is the difference between a physical change and a chemical change? (pp. 65–72)

Motivation   Refer students to the lesson opener picture on page 65 and ask the following questions:

1. What is the man doing? Is he changing the chemical make-up of the wood?

2. What is happening to the wood in the circle of stones? Do you think its chemical make-up changes as it burns?

Demonstration   Introduce this lesson by performing some simple physical changes and chemical changes. To show a physical change, cut an apple in half or crumple up a piece of paper. To demonstrate a chemical change, burn a match or a small piece of paper. Point out that a chemical change results in new substances.

Demonstration   Use a ball-and-stick molecular model kit to show the changes that take place during a chemical reaction.

LESSON 12
How is a mixture different from a compound? (pp. 73–79)

Motivation   Refer students to the lesson opener picture on page 73 and ask the following questions:

1. What is the person doing?

2. Are the salt and pepper being combined chemically?

Laboratory Experiment   Making a Mixture and a Compound

Materials   measuring cup (which has never been used in a lab before), teaspoon, water, table salt, 6-volt lantern battery, two pieces of insulated wire (about 10" long) with 1" of insulation removed from both ends, two large steel nails, small jar (big enough to hold the nails), saltwater mixture

Procedure   Allow one class period for the performances of parts I and II of this activity. Students may work in groups. They should carefully follow the directions given in the lesson.

Class Activity   Give each student a glass filled with a mixture of two common objects (such as paper clips and rubber bands). Ask the students to separate the items. Then give each student a glass of water. Ask the students if they can physically separate the water into hydrogen and oxygen. Ask the students to identify each glass as containing a mixture or a compound.

LESSON 13
How can mixtures be separated? (pp. 81–88)

Motivation   Refer students to the lesson opener picture on page 81 and ask the following questions:

1. How could you use a magnet to separate magnetic substances out of a mixture?

2. What is this little girl doing?

Demonstration Make a mixture of salt water. Heat the salt water to show students how a mixture can be separated by evaporation.

Class Activity Divide the class into five groups. Give each group one of the mixtures listed on page 87 and the materials necessary to separate the mixture. Have each group separate their mixture.

LESSON 14
What is a suspension? (pp. 89–96)

Motivation Refer students to the lesson opener picture on page 89 and ask the following questions:

1. What property of a suspension is shown in the picture of the jar?

2. Is a suspension a mixture?

Demonstration Add some soil to a jar of water to make a suspension. Ask students to describe the mixture. Then allow the mixture to stand for a while and have students observe what happens. Students will observe that the soil particles settle to the bottom.

Reinforcement Be sure students understand that some emulsions, such as homogenized milk, are also colloids, since they are permanent suspensions.

LESSON 15
How can the parts of a suspension be separated? (pp. 97–104)

Motivation Refer students to the lesson opener picture on page 97 and ask the following questions:

1. Why would you want to separate a suspension?

2. What methods of separating suspensions are shown in the two pieces of art?

Demonstration Demonstrate that the size of particles determines the rate at which the particles settle. Place clay, sand, and 0.025-cm glass beads in a 100-mL graduated cylinder. Fill the graduated cylinder with water, cover the top, and shake the mixture. Allow the mixture to stand overnight. Have students observe the mixture the next day. Students will observe three layers of sediment: clay on top, sand in the middle, and the glass beads on the bottom. Ask students which substance has the smallest particles.

Demonstration Demonstrate filtration by filtering some clay out of a water suspension.

Extension Spinning in a high-speed centrifuge created increased forces due to the centrifugal, or centripetal, forces. The increased forces speed up the settling process, thus separating the suspension.

LESSON 16
What is a solution? (pp. 105–110)

Motivation Refer students to the lesson opener picture on page 105 and ask the following questions:

1. Is a solution a mixture?

2. Is ocean water a solution?

Reinforcement Remind students that a mixture is made up of two or more substances that are not chemically combined.

Demonstration Add some salt to water in a test tube. Add sand to water in another test tube. Have students observe the difference in the two mixtures. Elicit from students that the salt dissolved in the water, but the sand did not. Use this demonstration to introduce the definition of a solution.

Reinforcement Students often confuse the words solute and solvent. Be sure students are clear of the definitions of each word.

LESSON 17
What are the properties of solutions? (pp. 111–116)

Motivation Refer students to the lesson opener picture on page 111 and ask the following questions:

1. Are all solutions transparent?

2. What is the solute in salt water?

Reteaching Option Exhibit the following mixtures in front of the classroom: sugar and water, iron filings and water, sulfur and water. Have students observe the mixtures. Point out that not all substances dissolve in water. Explain that substances that dissolve in water are soluble in water. Substances that do not dissolve in water are insoluble in water.

Reinforcement Be sure students understand that substances are soluble or insoluble only in terms of another substance.

LESSON 18
How can the strength of a solution be changed? (pp. 117–123)

Motivation Refer students to the lesson opener picture on page 117 and ask the following questions:

1. What is the difference between the three beakers of solutions?

2. Which beaker of solution is the most saturated?

Discussion Prepare solutions of either instant coffee or tea in varying concentrations and display the solutions in front of the classroom. Ask students to state how the solutions differ. Elicit the response that the darker solutions contain more solute and the lighter solutions contain less solute. Point out that weak solutions are called dilute solutions and strong solutions are called concentrated solutions.

LESSON 19
How can solutes be made to dissolve faster? (pp. 125–130)

Motivation Refer students to the lesson opener picture on page 125 and ask the following questions:

1. Which will dissolve faster — a cube of sugar or granulated sugar in a glass of water?

2. Do you think hot water will make a solute dissolve faster?

Demonstration Demonstrate how temperature affects the rate at which a solid solute dissolves by placing a spoonful of sugar into each of two beakers, one containing hot water and the other containing cold water. Stir the beakers simultaneously until the solute completely dissolves in one of the beakers. Students will observe that sugar dissolves faster in hot water.

Demonstration Demonstrate that particle size affects the rate of dissolving by placing some large crystals of copper sulfate into one beaker of water and some pulverized crystals into a second beaker of water. Stir both beakers until the solute completely dissolves in one beaker.

LESSON 20
How can solutes change the freezing and boiling point of water? (pp. 131–136)

Motivation Refer students to the lesson opener picture on page 131 and ask the following questions:

1. How does antifreeze affect the freezing and boiling point?

2. How do you think rock salt works?

Laboratory Experiment How does salt change the boiling point of water?

Materials 2 beakers, 2 ring stands and clamps, 2 thermometers, water, salt, 2 Bunsen burners

Advance Preparation Obtain enough Bunsen burners and thermometers for use in this experiment.

Caution: Tell students to be careful when working with the Bunsen burner as well as the glassware.

Discussion Provide motivation for this lesson by exhibiting a bag of rock salt in front of the classroom. Ask students when rock salt is used. Then ask students how they think rock salt affects ice. Point out that the salt itself does not cause the ice to melt. Instead, the salt dissolves in the thin film of water that forms when the ice begins to melt. Point out that as the salt dissolves in the film of water, the freezing point of water is lowered. Thus, the ice is less likely to refreeze. Identify rock salt as one application of freezing point depression.

Demonstration Pour 100 mL of distilled water into each of the two beakers. Add 10g of salt to one of the beakers. Put a thermometer into each beaker. Then heat the beakers until the solutions boil. Have students note that the presence of salt raises the boiling point of water. Identify this property as boiling point elevation.

LESSON 21
How can the parts of a solution be separated? (pp. 137–142)

Motivation Refer students to the lesson opener picture on page 137 and ask the following questions:

1. What is happening to the solution in the petri dishes?

2. What is happening in the other figure?

Laboratory Experiment Can filtering separate a solute from a solvent?

Materials 2 beakers, copper sulfate solution, funnel, filter paper, ring stand

Advance Preparation Obtain enough copper sulfate solution for use in this experiment.

Caution: Tell students to be careful when working with copper sulfate, as well as glassware.

Demonstration Place 10 mL of a copper sulfate solution in an evaporating dish. Heat the solution until the water boils away. Exhibit the residue of $CuSO_4$ crystals. Point out that a solute can be recovered from a solution by evaporating the solvent.

LESSON 22
What are acids? (pp. 143–148)

Motivation Refer students to the lesson opener picture on page 143 and ask the following questions:

1. What are some acids you can name?

2. Are any acids found naturally in the body?

Discussion Provide motivation for this lesson by exhibiting several substances that contain acids, such as vinegar, lemons, and sour cream. Ask students to describe the taste of these different substances. (Do not allow students to taste the substances.) Elicit the response that each substance tastes sour. Point out that each substance tastes sour because it contains acids. Define an acid as a substance that reacts with a metal to release hydrogen. Then describe the other properties of acids. Relate the properties of acids to the presence of hydrogen.

Reinforcement Review the acids listed in the chart on page 145. Ask students to identify the elements that make up each acid and the number of atoms of each element that combine to form one molecule of the acid. Emphasize that acids can be recognized by the fact that the symbol for hydrogen appears first in the chemical formula.

LESSON 23
What are bases? (pp. 149–154)

Motivation Refer students to the lesson opener picture on page 149 and ask the following questions:

1. What bases can you name?

2. What base do you use daily?

Discussion Exhibit some substances containing bases in front of the classroom, such as a bar of soap, milk of magnesia, ammonia, and limewater. Tell students that each substance contains a base. Define a base as a substance that is formed when a metal reacts with water. Wet the bar of soap and hand it to a student. Ask the student to describe the feel of the soap. Explain that the slippery feel of soap is caused by the base it contains.

Reinforcement Refer students to the chart on page 151. Tell students to study the chemical formulas of the bases listed in the table. Ask students what all the bases have in common. Explain that all bases contain hydroxyl ions, which they release in water.

LESSON 24
What happens when acids and bases are mixed? (pp. 155–160)

Motivation Refer students to the lesson opener picture on page 155 and ask the following questions:

1. What does the equation show?

2. What is the scientist doing?

Discussion Display a bottle of table salt on your desk. Point out that table salt is just one of many different salts. Explain that a salt is produced when an acid reacts with a base. Write the neutralization reaction that takes place between hydrochloric acid and sodium hydroxide on the chalkboard and guide students through the equation.

Demonstration To demonstrate that a neutralization reaction results in a neutral substance, test a solution of table salt and water with red litmus paper and blue litmus paper. Students will observe that the indicators do not change color.

Reinforcement Bring an antacid to class. Hold it up in front of the classroom and ask students what antacids are used to treat. Point out that an antacid is a base, which neutralizes stomach acids. Then describe neutralization reactions in general.

LESSON 25
Why do some liquids conduct electricity? (pp. 161–166)

Motivation Refer students to the lesson opener picture on page 161 and ask the following questions:

1. What is shown in the pictures?

2. Do acids and bases conduct electricity?

Demonstration Set up a conductivity tester as shown in the diagram on page 163. Place some distilled water in the test tube and have students observe that the bulb does not light. Then add some acetic acid to the water. Students will observe that the bulb lights when acetic acid is added. Use this demonstration to introduce electrolytes and ionization.

LESSON 26
What are oxidation numbers? (pp. 167–174)

Motivation Refer students to the lesson opener picture on page 167 and ask the following questions:

1. What two compounds are shown here?

2. What elements make up these compounds?

Reinforcement Students often associate the term "gains" with a plus sign and the term "loses" with a minus sign. Be sure students understand that an atom that gains electrons has a negative oxidation number and an atom that loses electrons has a positive oxidation number.

LESSON 27
What is a polyatomic ion? (pp. 175–178)

Motivation Refer students to the lesson opener picture on page 175 and ask the following questions:

1. What ions are pictured here?

2. What atoms make up these ions?

Class Activity Have students look up the meaning of the prefix "poly-" in a dictionary. Then relate the meaning of the prefix "poly-" to its usage in the term "polyatomic ion."

Reinforcement Be sure students understand that when polyatomic ions take part in a chemical reaction, these groups of atoms behave as if they were a single unit. Tell students to treat polyatomic ions and their oxidation numbers in the same way as a single atom when writing chemical formulas.

LESSON 28
What is a polyvalent element? (pp. 179–182)

Motivation Refer students to the lesson opener picture on page 179 and ask the following questions:

1. What are the two compounds pictured here?

2. What are the differences between these two compounds?

Reinforcement Write the formulas for ferric chloride ($FeCl_3$) and ferrous chloride ($FeCl_2$) on the board. Ask students what the oxidation number of the iron (Fe) in each compound is.

Discussion You may wish to tell students that electrons in the outer shell are called valance electrons. Valance is another term for oxidation number. Therefore, "polyvalent" literally means "having more than one oxidation number."

LESSON 29
What is formula mass? (pp. 183–188)

Motivation Refer students to the lesson opener picture on page 183 and ask the following questions:

1. What is the atomic mass of sodium?

2. What is the atomic mass of chlorine?

Reinforcement Review the concept of atomic mass. Have students recall that the atomic mass of an atom is equal to the total number of protons and neutrons in its nucleus.

Discussion Describe the formula mass of a molecule. Point out that a molecule contains one or more atoms. From this, develop the idea that the mass of one molecule is equivalent to the total mass of the atoms that make up the molecule.

LESSON 30
What is a chemical equation? (pp. 189–194)

Motivation Refer students to the lesson opener picture on page 189 and ask the following questions:

1. What is shown in the first picture?

2. What compound is being formed in the chemical equation shown here?

Reinforcement Remind students to use oxidation numbers to write correct chemical formulas.

Extension To help students understand chemical equations, you may wish to compare chemical equations with addition problems. Relate the reactants to the addends, the arrow to the equal sign, and the products to the sum.

LESSON 31
Does a chemical reaction destroy matter? (pp. 195–202)

Motivation Refer students to the lesson opener picture on page 195 and ask the following questions:

1. What object is shown in the top picture?

2. What happened in the bottom two pictures?

Laboratory Experiment Proving conservation of matter

Materials small plastic container, vinegar, baking soda, small sealable plastic bag, teasoon, balance scale

Procedure This experiment takes approximately 30 minutes. Students may work together in small groups or the experiment may be done as a demonstration. Tell students to be careful when they flash the bulb.

Reinforcement Review the differences between a physical change and chemical change. Then ask students which type of change results in new substances. Define a chemical reaction as the process by which new substances are formed.

LESSON 32
What is a synthesis reaction? (pp. 203–208)

Motivation Refer students to the lesson opener picture on page 203 and ask the following questions:

1. What happened to the train in the top two pictures?

2. What happened to the atoms in the bottom picture?

Reinforcement Using common materials such as children's building blocks or pegs, make models illustrating synthesis reactions.

LESSON 33
What is a decomposition reaction? (pp. 209–214)

Motivation Refer students to the lesson opener picture on page 209 and ask the following questions:

1. What happened to the truck in the top picture?

2. What happened to the NaCl in the bottom picture?

Demonstration Decompose water with a Hoffman apparatus. (A small amount of sulfuric acid should be added to the water in the apparatus to speed up the reaction.) After the apparatus has operated for some time, point out that one tube of the apparatus contains about twice as much gas as the other tube. Write the equation for decomposition of water $(2H_2O \rightarrow 2H_2 + O_2)$ on the chalkboard. Tell students that the tube with more gas in it contains hydrogen and the other tube contains oxygen.

Reinforcement Compare decomposition reactions with synthesis reactions. Point out that the two reactions are opposite. In synthesis reactions, simple substances combine to produce more complex substances. In decomposition reactions, more complex substances break down to produce simpler substances.

LESSON 34
What is a replacement reaction? (pp. 215–220)

Motivation Refer students to the lesson opener picture on page 215 and ask the following questions:

1. What is the difference between the trains in the two top pictures?

2. What is different in the bottom two pictures?

Laboratory Experiment Understanding single replacement reactions

Materials iron nail, copper sulfate solution, beaker

Advance Preparation Prepare the copper sulfate solution.

Procedure This experiment takes approximately 15 minutes. Students may work together in small groups or the experiment may be done as a demonstration. Caution students to be careful when working with the copper sulfate solution. Have students wash their hands when the experiment is completed.

Demonstration Neutralization reactions provide excellent demonstrations of double-replacement reaction.

Class Activity Have three students "act out" the examples of single-replacement reactions as shown in the lesson opener text.

LESSON 35
What are oxidation and reduction? (pp. 221–227)

Motivation Refer students to the lesson opener picture on page 221 and ask the following questions:

1. What is shown in the left picture?

2. What is happening in the right picture?

Discussion Students may be confused by the definition of the term "reduction" because the terms "reduced" and "gains" are usually thought of as opposites. Associate the term "reduction" with the negative charge of an electron to help students better understand its scientific meaning.

Reinforcement Be sure students understand that oxidation and reduction can take place without oxygen taking part in the reaction. Emphasize this concept by writing the redox reaction between sodium and chlorine on the chalkboard: $2Na + Cl_2 \rightarrow 2NaCl$.

SCIENCE WORKSHOP SERIES

Physical Science

CHEMICAL CHANGES

Seymour Rosen

GLOBE FEARON

Pearson Learning Group

THE AUTHOR

Seymour Rosen received his B.A. and M.S. degrees from Brooklyn College. He taught science in the New York City School System for twenty-seven years. Mr. Rosen was also a contributing participant in a teacher-training program for the development of science curriculum for the New York City Board of Education.

Cover Designer: Joan Jacobus
Cover Photograph: Dennis McColeman/Tony Stone Images
Cover Photo Researcher: Martin Levick
Photo Researchers: Rhoda Sidney, Jenifer Hixson

About the cover illustration: A firecracker is made of a paper and cardboard cylinder filled with an explosive. When the fuse is lit, the firecracker explodes.

Photo Credits:

p. 3, Fig. G: Bethlehem Steel
p. 4, Fig. H: Cunard Lines
p. 4, Fig. I: General Motors
p. 4, Fig. J: Bayer/Monkmeyer Press
p. 14, Fig. K: Mimi Forsyth/Monkmeyer Press
p. 14, Fig. L: Mimi Forsyth/Monkmeyer Press
p. 32, Fig. C: NASA
p. 70, Fig. G: William Frost
p. 71, Fig. H: UPI
p. 80: Hugh Rogers/Monkmeyer Press
p. 94, Fig. F: The Image Works Archives
p. 124: Charles D. Winters/Photo Researchers
p. 136, Fig. F: Gary Walts/The Image Works
p. 146, Fig. B: Gerard Fritz/Monkmeyer Press
p. 146, Fig. C: Rhoda Sidney
p. 152, Fig. C: Rhoda Sidney
p. 152, Fig. D: Arlene Collins/Monkmeyer Press
p. 152, Fig. E: Fredrik D. Bodin/Stock Boston
p. 152, Fig. F: Grant Heilman
p. 182, Fig. A: Helena Frost
p. 202, Fig. I: Department of Energy
p. 223, Fig. A: Helena Frost
p. 223, Fig. B: Helena Frost
p. 228: Bob Daemmrich/The Image Works

ISBN 0-130-23389-7 (Student Edition)
Printed in the United States of America
3 4 5 6 7 8 9   06 05 04 03 02

1-800-321-3106
www.pearsonlearning.com

CONTENTS

HEAT

1. What is heat? — 1

2. How does heat change the size of matter? — 7

3. How does heat move through solids? — 15

4. How does heat move through liquids and gases? — 21

5. How does heat move through empty space? — 27

6. What is the difference between heat and temperature? — 33

7. How does a thermometer work? — 39

COMPOUNDS

8. What are compounds? — 45

9. What is a chemical formula? — 51

10. How do elements form compounds? — 57

11. What is the difference between a physical change and a chemical change? — 65

MIXTURES

12. How is a mixture different from a compound? — 73

SCIENCE **EXTRA** – Buckyballs — 80

13. How can mixtures be separated? — 81

14. What is a suspension? — 89

15. How can the parts of a suspension be separated? — 97

SOLUTIONS

16. What is a solution? — 105

17. What are the properties of solutions? — 111

18. How can the strength of a solution be changed? — 117

SCIENCE *EXTRA* – Crystals 124

19. How can solutes be made to dissolve faster? 125

20. How can solutes change the freezing and boiling point of water? ... 131

21. How can the parts of a solution be separated? 137

ACIDS AND BASES

22. What are acids? 143

23. What are bases? 149

24. What happens when acids and bases are mixed? 155

25. Why do some liquids conduct electricity? 161

CHEMICAL REACTIONS

26. What are oxidation numbers? 167

27. What is a polyatomic ion? 175

28. What is a polyvalent element? 179

29. What is formula mass? 183

30. What is a chemical equation? 189

31. Does a chemical reaction destroy matter? 195

32. What is a synthesis reaction? 203

33. What is a decomposition reaction? 209

34. What is a replacement reaction? 215

35. What are oxidation and reduction? 221

SCIENCE *EXTRA* – Pharmacist 228

THE METRIC SYSTEM 229

PERIODIC TABLE OF ELEMENTS 230

SAFETY ALERT SYMBOLS 232

GLOSSARY/INDEX 233

Introduction to Chemical Changes

"Things change." "People change." "The more things change the more they stay the same."

You have heard these phrases. You probably have even used them yourself. People spend a lot of time talking about changes. You say "What's new?" when you see a friend. Every night on television, there are news programs to tell you what has happened that day.

Changes are what keeps life from being boring. If everything were exactly the same all the time, nothing would happen.

Fortunately, things do change. When they do, we need to understand the changes so we can change as well.

Scientists, like everyone else, are interested in changes. They study changes. They try to figure out how changes occur and why they happen.

This book is about chemical changes. Read it and you will understand a little bit more about the world around you. And you will be ready for the changes.

What is heat?

KEY TERMS

heat: form of energy in moving particles of matter

friction: force that opposes the motion of an object

LESSON 1 | What is heat?

Here is a trick question—Does an ice cube have heat? Think carefully! The answer is YES! An ice cube does have heat. It has <u>less</u> heat than water does, but it still has heat. All matter has heat. Some kinds of matter have more heat than other kinds.

WHAT IS HEAT?

Heat is a form of energy.

Heat is the energy of vibrating particles — and particles are always vibrating. This means that all matter has heat.

How hot an object is depends on how fast its particles vibrate. The faster the particles vibrate, the hotter the object is.

WHERE DOES HEAT COME FROM?

The sun provides most of our heat. The sun warms our earth. It makes plants and trees grow. Without the sun, we would have no food. And we need food to live. There can be no life without heat.

Burning fuel provides some heat. Coal, oil, gas, and wood are some fuels that we burn. But without the sun, these fuels would not have formed.

Rubbing—or **friction**—also provides heat. Most heat that comes from friction is not wanted. For example, heat from friction can ruin machinery. Oil and grease help reduce friction.

Figure A *Particles are always vibrating.*

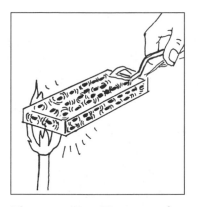

Figure B *Heat makes particles vibrate faster.*

Figure C *When matter cools, its particles vibrate more slowly.*

SOURCES OF HEAT

Figure D *The sun*

Figure E *Burning fuel*

Figure F *Friction*

Figure G

Nuclear reactions can give off a tremendous amount of heat. We are just learning how to use this technology.

In nuclear power plants, certain kinds of atoms are split. When they divide, they give up energy in the form of heat. This heat changes water to steam. The steam turns the coils in generators, which produce electricity.

ENERGY CAN MAKE THINGS MOVE

There are many kinds of energy. Heat is one kind of energy. Heat can make things move.

Figure H

Figure I

Heat moves ocean liners, diesel trucks—even your family car.

How does this happen?

1. Ocean liners, diesel trucks, and automobile engines burn fuel.
2. Fuel has stored chemical energy. The chemical energy changes to heat energy.
3. The high temperature causes great pressure.
4. The force of the pressure is used to move the vehicle.

Figure J

Heat has thousands of other uses too. For example, we use heat to warm our homes and to cook our food. Doctors use heat to kill germs. Heat is used to make metal products.

FILL IN THE BLANK

Complete each statement using a term or terms from the list below. Write your answers in the spaces provided. Some words may be used more than once.

energy	more	vibrating particles
sun	move	heat
vibrating	friction	less

1. Energy can make things _____move_____ .

2. Heat is a form of _____energy_____ .

3. Heat is caused by _____vibrating particles_____ .

4. All matter has _____heat_____ because particles are always _____vibrating_____ .

5. Warm matter has _____more_____ heat than cold matter.

6. Cool matter has _____less_____ heat than warm matter.

7. The faster particles vibrate, the _____more_____ heat they give off.

8. The slower particles vibrate, the _____less_____ heat they give off.

9. Most heat comes from the _____sun_____ .

10. Rubbing produces heat. Another name for rubbing is _____friction_____ .

MATCHING

Match each term in Column A with its description in Column B. Write the correct letter in the space provided.

	Column A	Column B
__d__ 1.	friction	a) gives us most of our heat
__a__ 2.	sun	b) examples of fuel
__e__ 3.	vibrating particles	c) can make things move
__c__ 4.	energy	d) rubbing
__b__ 5.	coal, wood, oil, gas	e) cause all heat

TRUE OR FALSE

In the space provided, write "true" if the sentence is true. Write "false" if the sentence is false.

True	**1.**	All particles vibrate.
False	**2.**	Particles always vibrate at the same speed.
False	**3.**	The faster particles vibrate, the less heat they give off.
False	**4.**	Most of our heat comes from the moon.
True	**5.**	Coal, wood, oil, and gas are fuels.
True	**6.**	Without the sun, we would have no coal, wood, oil, or gas.
True	**7.**	A piece of dust has heat.
True	**8.**	A flame always gives off heat.
False	**9.**	Heat always gives off a flame.
True	**10.**	Heat can do work.

WORD SCRAMBLE

Below are several scrambled words you have used in this Lesson. Unscramble the words and write your answers in the spaces provided.

1. REGYEN   ENERGY
2. LUFE   FUEL
3. TROCINIF   FRICTION
4. TEAH   HEAT
5. BUNGBIR   RUBBING

How does heat change the size of matter?

KEY TERMS

expand: make larger

contract: make smaller

LESSON 2 | How does heat change the size of matter?

Household hint: If you cannot open the lid of a jar, hold the lid under hot water for about a minute. Then, try again to turn the lid. Usually, it works! Why does the hot water work? The answer is simple. The heat makes the lid a tiny bit <u>larger</u>. Then, it is easier to turn.

HEAT MAKES THINGS LARGER.

As you know, matter is made up of atoms and molecules. And they are always vibrating. The greater the heat, the faster they vibrate. When molecules vibrate faster, they need more room. They make more room by s–p–r–e–a–d–i–n–g o–u–t. The heated matter becomes larger. It **expands**.

When matter cools, the opposite happens. The molecules vibrate slower. Now they need less room. They move closer together. This makes the matter smaller. It **contracts**.

Most matter:

• expands when heated.

• contracts when cooled.

Temperature is always changing. It becomes warmer and cooler over and over again. As a result, the size of matter is always changing too. Usually, matter expands or contracts only slightly. Other times, size changes a lot. Slight changes are usually not important. Large changes can be very important. For example, when heat expands a roadway, the roadway can buckle. Heat expansion can make drawbridges stick.

Different kinds of matter expand at different rates. Some matter expands a great deal. Other matter expands only a little.

HOW DO HEAT AND COLD CHANGE THE SIZE OF A SOLID?

What You Need (Materials)

brass ring
brass ball that "just" fits through the ring
Bunsen burner
cold water

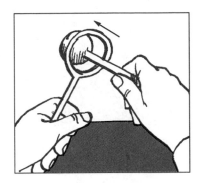

Figure A

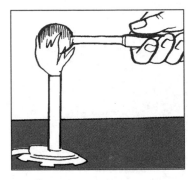

Figure B

Figure C

How to Do the Experiment

1. Pass the brass ball through the ring. Notice the close fit (Figure A).

2. Heat the ball over the flame for about one minute (Figure B).

3. Now try to pass the ball through the ring (Figure C).

What You Learned (Observations)

4. The heated ball _____did not_____ pass through the ring.

did, did not

5. The heat made the ball _____larger_____ .

smaller, larger

6. The ball _____expanded_____ .

expanded, contracted

Next Steps

cold water

Figure D

Figure E

7. Dip the heated ball into the cold water (Figure D).

8. Try to pass the ball through the ring (Figure E).

What You Learned (Observations)

9. After the ball cooled, it _____did_____ pass through the ring.
    did, did not

10. The cold water made the ball _____smaller_____.
    smaller, larger

11. The ball _____contracted_____.
    expanded, contracted

Something To Think About (Conclusions)

12. Heat _____expands_____ a solid.
    expands, contracts

13. Cold _____contracts_____ a solid.
    expands, contracts

MATCHING

Match each term in Column A with its description in Column B. Write the correct letter in the space provided.

	Column A		Column B
__c__	1. particles	**a)**	makes particles vibrate faster
__a__	2. heat	**b)**	sun
__e__	3. cold	**c)**	always vibrating
__d__	4. states of matter	**d)**	solids, liquids, gases
__b__	5. source of most heat	**e)**	makes particles vibrate slower
__h__	6. expand	**f)**	to make smaller
__f__	7. contract	**g)**	expand when heated
__g__	8. solids	**h)**	to make larger

HOW DO HEAT AND COLD CHANGE THE SIZE OF A LIQUID?

What You Need (Materials)

Pyrex bottle
cold, colored water
one-holed stopper with glass tube
warm water
large beaker

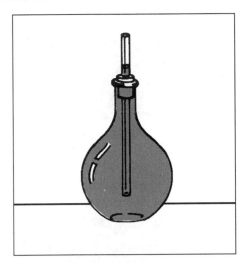

Figure F

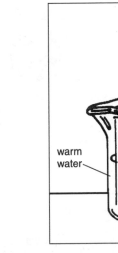

warm water

Figure G

How to Do the Experiment (Procedure)

1. Put cold, colored water in the bottle. Cap the bottle with the one-holed stopper. Put a glass tube through the hole of the stopper and into the water (Figure F).

2. Heat the bottle gently by placing it in a container of warm water (Figure G). Then take the bottle out of the warm water. (Watch the water level in the tube.)

What You Learned (Observations)

3. When you heated the bottle, the water in the tube moved ____up____ .
   _{up, down}

4. The water rose because it ____expanded____ .
   _{expanded, contracted}

5. When you took away the heat, the water became ____cooler____ .
   _{cooler, warmer}

6. The water moved ____down____ in the tube.
   _{up, down}

7. The water moved down because it ____contracted____ .
   _{expanded, contracted}

Something To Think About (Conclusions)

8. When a liquid is heated it ____expands____ .
   _{expands, contracts}

9. When a liquid cools, it ____contracts____ .
   _{expands, contracts}

HOW DO HEAT AND COLD CHANGE THE SIZE OF GAS?

What You Need (Materials)

Pyrex bottle
cold, colored water
one-holed stopper
glass tube with bulb

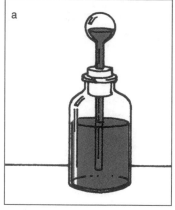

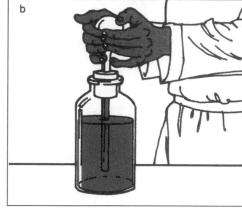

Figure H   Figure I

How to Do the Experiment (Procedure)

1. Set up the equipment as shown (Figure H).

2. Heat the bulb gently by wrapping your hands around it (Figure I). Keep your hands around the bulb for at least one minute. Then take your hands away. Watch the water level in the tube.

What You Learned (Observations)

3. There is mostly _____gas_____ in the bulb.
   _{water, gas}

4. When you heated the bulb, the gas took up _____more_____ room.
   _{more, less}

5. The gas _____expanded_____ .
   _{expanded, contracted}

6. The expanded gas made the water in the tube _____move down_____ .
   _{rise, move down}

7. When you took away the heat, the gas _____became cooler_____ .
   _{became warmer, became cooler}

8. The gas _____contracted_____ .
   _{expanded, contracted}

9. The gas pressed on the water with _____less_____ force.
   _{more, less}

10. The water in the tube moved _____up_____ .
    _{up, down}

Something to Think About (Conclusions)

11. When a gas is heated, it _____expands_____ .
    _{expands, contracts}

12. When a gas cools, it _____contracts_____ .
    _{expands, contracts}

12

EXCEPTIONS

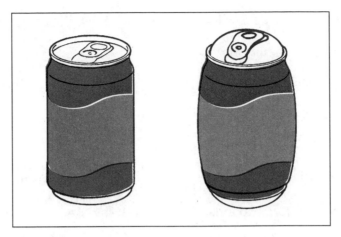

Figure J

You have learned that matter expands when heated and contracts when cooled. But there are <u>exceptions</u>.

For example, water contracts as its temperature drops. BUT when it changes to solid ice, it expands.

FILL IN THE BLANK

Complete each statement using a term or terms from the list below. Write your answers in the spaces provided. Some words may be used more than once.

expand	heated	more
contracts	become smaller	become larger
heat	less	vibrating

1. Most matter expands when _____heated_____ .

2. Particles are always _____vibrating_____ .

3. Vibrating particles give off _____heat_____ .

4. When particles vibrate faster, they give off _____more_____ heat.

5. When particles vibrate faster, they need _____more_____ room.

6. Heat makes matter _____expand_____ in size.
   (one word)

7. When particles vibrate slower, they give off _____less_____ heat.

8. When particles vibrate slower, they need _____less_____ room.

9. Matter that cools _____contracts_____ in size.
   (one word)

10. Expand means _____become larger_____ ; contract means _____become smaller_____ .

TRUE OR FALSE

In the space provided, write "true" if the sentence is true. Write "false" if the sentence is false.

True	**1.**	All particles vibrate.
False	**2.**	The slower particles vibrate, the more heat they give off.
False	**3.**	Matter contracts when it is heated.
True	**4.**	Matter contracts when it is cooled.
False	**5.**	All matter expands and contracts the same amount.
False	**6.**	When matter expands, it takes up less room.
False	**7.**	When matter contracts, it takes up more room.
True	**8.**	Liquid water expands as it changes to ice.
False	**9.**	All matter expands as it cools.
True	**10.**	Some matter expands only a little when it is heated.

REACHING OUT

Figure K   **Figure L**

1. Why do overhead wires hang with a slight sag in the summertime? _____

The summer heat expands wires.

2. Why do the same wires hang tightly during the wintertime? _____

The winter cold contracts wires.

14

Heat

How does heat move through solids?

KEY TERMS

conduction: the way heat moves through solids

conductors: substances that conduct heat easily

insulators: substances that do not conduct heat easily

LESSON 3 | How does heat move through solids?

Did you every grab a hot pan handle? The handle was hot even though it wasn't over the burner. How did the heat move to the handle?

First, the bottom of the pan became hot. The particles there vibrated faster and faster. As they vibrated, they bumped into other particles. Then, the other particles became hot, vibrated faster, and bumped into other particles.

This happened over and over again. As it did, the heat moved farther along. Soon, the entire pan was hot.

The passing along of heat from particle to particle is called **conduction** [kun-DUK-shun]. Only solids move heat by conduction.

In solids, the particles are packed very close together. They cannot move from place to place. The particles just vibrate faster and faster when a solid is heated.

All solids conduct heat. Some conduct heat much better than others. Solids that conduct heat well are called good **conductors**. Metals are the best heat conductors.

Wood, glass, and plastics do not conduct heat well. They are poor conductors. Poor conductors are used as **insulators**. Insulators keep heat from moving where it is not wanted. They keep things from becoming too hot or too cold. If the handle of the pan is covered by an insulator, you won't burn your hand.

Insulators protect us from heat and cold. They keep us comfortable.

HOW CONDUCTION TAKES PLACE

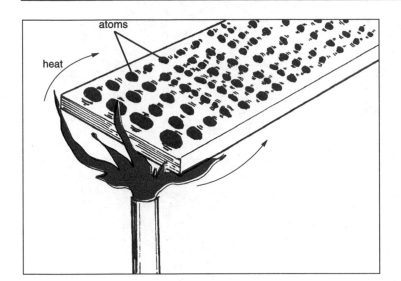

Figure A

Heat moves through solids by conduction.

In conduction, heat is passed along from particle to particle.

STUDYING CONDUCTION

Look at each picture. Then answer the questions for Figures B and C.

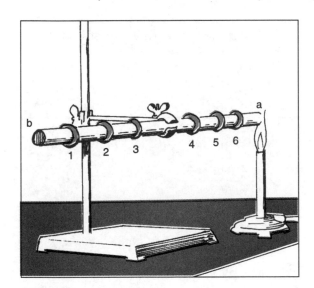

Figure B

Figure B shows six rings of wax on a metal rod. The flame has just been placed under the rod.

1. Which wax ring will melt first?

   _____6_____

2. Which wax ring will melt last?

   _____1_____

3. Which end gets hot first? _____a_____

4. Which end gets hot last? _____b_____

5. What do we call the way heat moves

   in solids? _____conduction_____

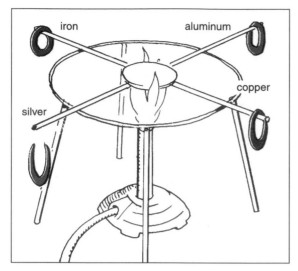

iron   aluminum

copper

silver

Figure C

Figure C shows wax rings at same distance from the flame.

6. Are all the wax rings melting at the same time? _____no_____

7. Are the rods made of the same metal? _____no_____

8. Which one of these rods is the best conductor of heat? _____silver_____

9. You know that it is the best conductor of heat because the wax melted around it
   _____first_____ .
   first, last

10. Which rod is the worst conductor of heat? _____iron_____

11. You know that it is the worst conductor of heat because the wax melts around it
    _____last_____ .
    first, last

12. This experiment shows that conduction is _____different for different solids_____ .
    the same for all solids, different for different solids

TRUE OR FALSE

In the space provided, write "true" if the sentence is true. Write "false" if the sentence is false.

True   1. All matter has heat.

True   2. Heat can move from place to place.

False   3. Particles vibrate slower when they are heated.

False   4. Heat moves through liquids and gases by conduction.

True   5. Conduction moves heat from particle to particle.

False   6. In conduction, particles move from place to place.

False   7. All solids are good conductors of heat.

True   8. Metals are good conductors of heat.

False   9. Metals are good insulators of heat.

True   10. Wood and plastics are good insulators of heat.

18

FILL IN THE BLANK

Complete each statement using a term or terms from the list below. Write your answers in the spaces provided.

insulator   faster   solids
vibrate   metals   heat
conduction   bump   do not
prevent   better

1. Heat makes particles vibrate _____faster_____ .

2. The faster particles vibrate, the more they _____bump_____ into other molecules.

3. When particles hit other particles, the other particles _____vibrate_____ faster and give off more _____heat_____ .

4. The passing of heat from particle to particle is called _____conduction_____ .

5. Only _____solids_____ move heat by conduction.

6. Particles of solids _____do not_____ move from place to place.

7. The best conductors of heat are _____metals_____ .

8. Some metals are _____better_____ heat conductors than others.

9. A poor conductor is called an _____insulator_____ .

10. The job of an insulator is to _____prevent_____ heat from being conducted.

MATCHING

Match each term in Column A with its description in Column B. Write the correct letter in the space provided.

	Column A	Column B
d	1. insulate	a) good heat conductors
a	2. metals	b) give off energy
e	3. conduction	c) poor heat conductors
c	4. plastics and wood	d) to prevent heat and cold from being conducted
b	5. vibrating molecules	e) the way heat moves in solids

WORD SEARCH

The list on the left contains words that you have used in this Lesson. Find and circle each word where it appears in the box. The spellings may go in any direction: up, down, left, right, or diagonally.

HEAT

SUN

FRICTION

ENERGY

FUEL

EXPAND

CONTRACT

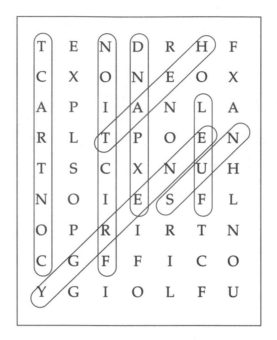

T	E	N	D	R	H	F
C	X	O	N	E	O	X
A	P	I	A	N	L	A
R	L	T	P	O	E	N
T	S	C	X	N	U	H
N	O	I	E	S	F	L
O	P	R	I	R	T	N
C	G	F	F	I	C	O
Y	G	I	O	L	F	U

REACHING OUT

An iron pot and a copper pot are the same size and shape. Both pots are heated.

1. Which pot will heat up faster? <u>the copper pot</u>

Both pots are heated to the same temperature and allowed to cool.

2. Which pot will cool faster? <u>the copper pot</u>

How does heat move through liquids and gases?

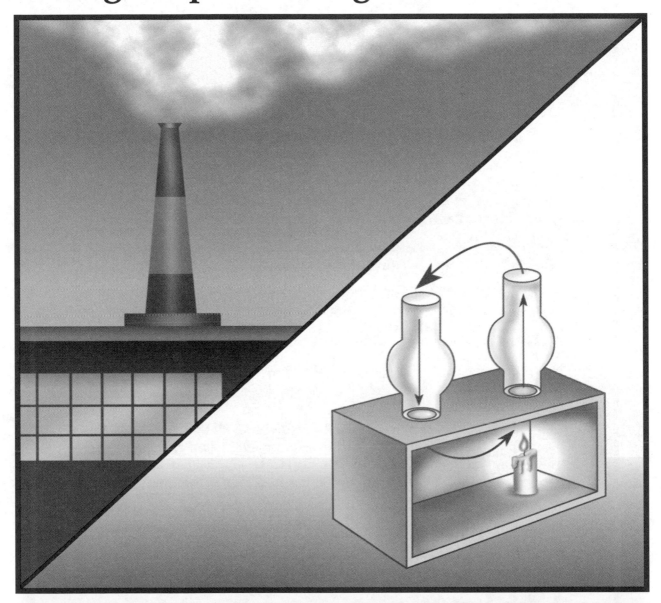

KEY TERM

convection: the way heat moves through liquids and gases

LESSON 4 | How does heat move through liquids and gases?

You have learned that the particles of solids are packed very close together. When a solid is heated, its particles vibrate faster, but they <u>cannot</u> move from place to place.

The particles of liquids and gases are <u>not</u> tightly packed. There are spaces between the particles. This means that the particles <u>can</u> move from place to place.

What happens when a liquid or gas is heated?

- The particles closest to the heat get hot first. They vibrate faster. They also move. They move away from the heat.

- Cooler particles move in and take their place.

- The cooler particles are heated. Then they move away.

- Other particles move in to take their place.

This happens over and over again. Little by little, all the particles in the gas or liquid are heated. The particles that were heated first cool a bit. Then they move back toward the heat and are heated again. This happens over and over—heating, cooling, and then reheating.

The passing along of heat by moving particles is called **convection** [kuhn-VEK-shun]. Only gases and liquids are heated by convection.

WHAT DO THE DIAGRAMS SHOW?

The diagrams below show atoms of solids, liquids, and gases. Study the diagrams. Then answer the questions below.

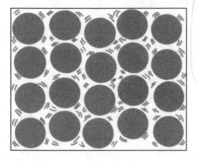
Figure A *Atoms of solids*

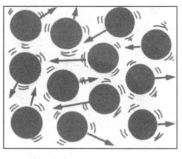
Figure B *Atoms of liquids*

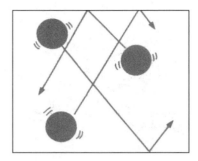
Figure C *Atoms of gases*

Which atoms . . .

1. are closest together? _____ solids _____

2. are farthest apart? _____ gases _____

3. vibrate? _____ all _____

4. do not vibrate? _____ none _____

5. do not move from place to place? _____ solids _____

6. move from place to place? _____ liquids and gases _____

7. move the most? _____ gases _____

8. become hot by conduction? _____ solids _____

9. become hot by convection? _____ liquids and gases _____

STUDYING CONVECTION IN A LIQUID

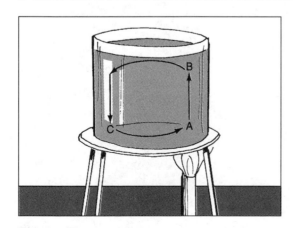

Figure D

1. The water at A is heated first. It rises to B.

2. As it rises, it cools a bit.

3. The cooled water turns around and drops to C. Then it moves to A again. Here it is reheated.

4. Now, start again with Step 1. Repeat the steps over and over and over again.

STUDYING CONVECTION IN GASES

Figure E

1. The sun heats the air. The air over the ground at A becomes warm first. It rises to B.

2. As it rises, it cools.

3. The cooler air turns around and drops to C. Then it moves to A again. Here it is reheated.

4. Now start again with Step 1. Repeat the steps over and over again.

When the air from A rises, other air from C moves in to take its place. What do you call

this kind of moving air? _____wind_____ (Take a guess. You know this term and use it often.)

This is called a convection box. The burning candle makes air move out of one chimney and into the other.

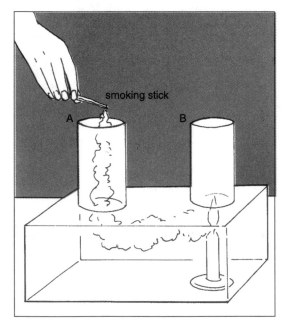

smoking stick

Figure F

1. Which air is warmer? The air in

   chimney _____B_____ .

                       A, B

2. Which air is cooler? The air in

   chimney _____A_____ .

                       A, B

3. Air in chimney B is _____rising_____ .

                       rising, falling

4. The air in chimney A is _____falling_____ .

                       rising, falling

5. Air is moving from _____A to B_____ .

                       A to B, B to A

6. Draw arrows to show how the air moves. Check students' diagrams.

FILL IN THE BLANK

Complete each statement using a term or terms from the list below. Write your answers in the spaces provided.

take their place	conduction	gases
convection	more	friction
cannot	solids	vibrating
sun	move away	

1. Particles of _____solids_____ are closest together.

2. Particles of _____gases_____ are farthest apart.

3. Heat moves through solids by a method called _____conduction_____ .

4. Heat moves through liquids and gases by a method called _____convection_____ .

5. Heat is caused by _____vibrating_____ molecules.

6. The faster particles vibrate, the _____more_____ heat they give off.

7. In conduction, vibrating particles _____cannot_____ move from place to place.

8. In convection, heated particles _____move away_____ and other particles _____take their place_____ .

9. Almost all of our heat energy comes from the _____sun_____ .

10. Another name for rubbing is _____friction_____ .

MATCHING

Match each term in Column A with its description in Column B. Write the correct letter in the space provided.

	Column A		Column B
__b__	1. conduction	**a)**	particles farthest apart
__d__	2. convection	**b)**	the way heat moves through solids
__e__	3. solids	**c)**	source of most of our energy
__a__	4. gases	**d)**	the way heat moves through liquids and gases
__c__	5. sun	**e)**	particles closest together

TRUE OR FALSE

In the space provided, write "true" if the sentence is true. Write "false" if the sentence is false.

False	**1.**	Only particles of solids vibrate.
False	**2.**	Particles of solids can move from place to place.
True	**3.**	Particles of liquids and gases can move from place to place.
True	**4.**	Particles of liquids are closer together than molecules of gases.
True	**5.**	Particles of solids are closer together than molecules of liquids.
True	**6.**	Heat makes particles vibrate faster.
True	**7.**	The faster particles vibrate, the more heat they give off.
False	**8.**	Cooling makes particles vibrate faster.
False	**9.**	All particles vibrate at the same speed.
True	**10.**	The sun heats the earth.

REACHING OUT

Why should a window be opened from the top <u>and</u> the bottom?

Accept all logical responses. Likely responses include that opening a window at the

top and the bottom will allow cool air to enter the room and warm air to leave the

room.

How does heat move through empty space?

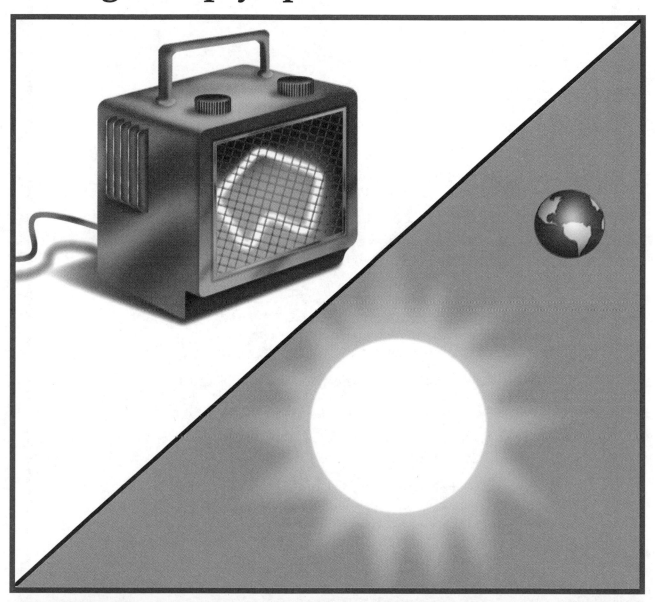

KEY TERMS

radiation: the way heat moves through empty space

reflect: bounce off

absorb: take in

LESSON 5 | How does heat move through empty space?

Can heat move where there is no matter?

You have learned that with conduction and convection, heat is carried by vibrating particles. And particles are matter.

Most of our heat comes from the sun. And the sun is 150 million kilometers (93 million miles) away. Most of this great distance is empty space. There are no particles there.

Then, how does the heat reach us?

There is a third way that heat travels. Heat moves through empty space by **radiation** [ray-dee-AY-shun]. Radiation needs no particles. The sun's heat reaches us by radiation.

When the sun's heat reaches the earth, two things happen.

- Part of the heat bounces off the surface of the earth. It is **reflected**.

- Part of the heat is taken in by the air, water, and land. It is **absorbed**. Matter warms up when it absorbs heat energy.

Radiation does not come only from outer space. Heat from a flame or a hot object reaches us by radiation. We would feel some of the heat even if there were no particles of air around us.

Figure A *Dark colors absorb heat.*

Figure B *Light colors reflect heat.*

1. This means that . . .

   a) dark colors _____become warmer_____ than light colors.
   become warmer, stay cooler

   b) light colors _____stay cooler_____ than dark colors.
   become warmer, stay cooler

2. In the winter, _____dark_____ colored clothing helps keep us warm.
   light, dark

3. In the summer, _____light_____ colored clothing helps keep us cool.
   light, dark

4. Would you wear dark colored clothing or light colored clothing if you lived near a desert or near the equator?

   _____light colored clothing_____

5. Would you wear dark colored clothing or light colored clothing if you lived in the far north or far south, that is, close to the poles?

   _____dark colored clothing_____

FILL IN THE BLANK

Complete each statement using a term or terms from the list below. Write your answers in the spaces provided. Some words may be used more than once.

reflect	conduction	matter
radiation	absorbed	absorb
convection	empty space	reflected

1. Heat moves through solids by a method called ___conduction___ .

2. Heat moves through liquids and gases by a method called ___convection___ .

3. In conduction and convection, heat moves through ___matter___ .

4. Between the sun and the earth there is mostly ___empty space___ .

5. Energy that can move through empty space is called ___radiation___ .

6. The sun's energy reaches us by a method called ___radiation___ .

7. Energy that is taken in is "___absorbed___ ."

8. Energy that bounces off is "___reflected___ ."

9. Dark colors ___absorb___ heat.

10. Light colors ___reflect___ heat.

CONDUCTION, CONVECTION, OR RADIATION?

Fill in each blank space with one or more of these terms.

1. The way heat moves through liquids and gases. ___convection___

2. The way heat reaches the moon. ___radiation___

3. The way heat moves through solids. ___conduction___

4. Heat-movement that needs no particles. ___radiation___

5. Heat-movements that need particles. ___conduction___ ___convection___

30

COMPLETING SENTENCES

Choose the correct word or term for each statement. Write your choice in the spaces provided.

1. Heat moves through solids by _____conduction_____ .
   conduction, convection, radiation

2. Heat moves through liquids by _____convection_____ .
   conduction, convection, radiation

3. Heat moves through gases by _____convection_____ .
   conduction, convection, radiation

4. Heat moves through empty space by _____radiation_____ .
   conduction, convection, radiation

5. Conduction _____does_____ need particles.
   does, does not

6. Convection _____does_____ need particles.
   does, does not

7. Radiation _____does not_____ need particles.
   does, does not

8. Heat that reaches the earth is _____absorbed or reflected_____ .
   absorbed only, reflected only, absorbed or reflected

9. Dark colors _____absorb_____ more heat than light colors.
   absorb, reflect

10. Light colors _____reflect_____ more heat than dark colors.
    absorb, reflect

WORD SCRAMBLE

Below are several scrambled words you have used in this Lesson. Unscramble the words and write your answers in the spaces provided.

1. DAITRONIA _____RADIATION_____

2. CONCONUTDI _____CONDUCTION_____

3. BRASBO _____ABSORB_____

4. FLERTCE _____REFLECT_____

5. TONICVECON _____CONVECTION_____

MATCHING

Match each term in Column A with its description in Column B. Write the correct letter in the space provided.

	Column A		Column B
c	**1.** conduction and convection	**a)**	absorb radiation
e	**2.** radiation	**b)**	always vibrating
a	**3.** dark colors	**c)**	need particles
d	**4.** light colors	**d)**	reflect radiation
b	**5.** particles	**e)**	needs no particles

REACHING OUT

Figure C

Objects in space are constantly being heated by the sun. These objects are covered with reflective materials to protect them from the heat of the sun.

How will this shiny material protect the satellite?

The material will reflect the heat, making it bounce off the satellite.

What is the difference between heat and temperature?

KEY TERMS

temperature: measure of how hot or cold something is

thermometer: instrument used to measure temperature

degree: unit used to measure temperature

calorie: unit used to measure heat

LESSON 6 | What is the difference between heat and temperature?

"What a hot day!"

"Gee! It's cold!"

"What's the temperature outside?"

"Ma! My head feels warm!"

We often talk about heat and temperature. Are they the same?

Heat and temperature are related. But they are not the same.

TEMPERATURE   The word **temperature** is used to describe how fast particles are moving. Temperature is measured with a **thermometer**. Temperature is measured in **degrees**. We use different thermometers to measure the temperatures of our bodies, the temperature outdoors, the temperature of an oven. But the measurement is always in degrees.

Temperature depends on how fast particles vibrate. The faster particles vibrate, the higher the temperature. The slower they vibrate, the lower the temperature.

HEAT   Heat is the total energy given off by all the vibrating particles in a bit of matter.

Heat depends on two things:

• How fast particles vibrate (temperature).

• How many particles vibrate.

This means that size affects the amount of heat. Larger things have more particles. So if you have a large object and a small object that both have the same temperature, the large object will have more heat.

Heat is measured in **calories** [KAL-uh-reez]. Have you heard that word before?

Test your understanding of temperature and heat. Study the figure below. Then answer the questions.

Figure A

Look at Figure A. Both the match flame and the water are hot. The flame has a higher temperature than boiling water.

1. Can a single match boil this much water? _____no_____

2. Which one do you think can melt more ice? _____the boiling water_____
   the burning match, the boiling water

3. Which has more heat? _____the boiling water_____
   the burning match, the boiling water

4. This shows that higher temperature _____does not_____ always mean more heat.
   does, does not

5. The boiling water has more heat because it has _____more molecules_____ .
   more molecules, a higher temperature

6. The term that describes how fast particles move is _____temperature_____ .
   calories, temperature

7. The term that described total heat energy is _____calories_____ .
   calories, temperature

35

Look at Figure B. Answer the following questions.

Figure B   *Both pots contain boiling water.*

8. The temperature of pot a is _____the same as_____ the temperature in pot b.
   <small>higher than, lower than, the same as</small>

9. The particles in pot a are vibrating _____at the same speed as_____ the particles in pot b.
   <small>more than, less than, at the same speed as</small>

10. Pot a and pot b _____do not_____ have the same number of calories.
    <small>do, do not</small>

11. _____Pot a_____ has fewer calories.
    <small>Pot a, Pot b</small>

12. _____Pot b_____ has more calories.
    <small>Pot a, Pot b</small>

FILL IN THE BLANK

Complete each statement using a term or terms from the list below. Write your answers in the spaces provided. Some words may be used more than once.

less heat	degrees	not
lower temperature	related	the number of particles
expand	higher temperature	more heat
how fast particles vibrate	calories	

1. Heat and temperature are _____related_____ but they are _____not_____ the same.

2. Temperature depends upon _____how fast particles vibrate_____.

3. Heat depends on _____how fast particles vibrate_____ and also on _____the number of particles_____ that vibrate.

4. Faster vibrating particles mean a _____higher temperature_____.

5. Slower vibrating particles usually mean _____lower temperature_____.

6. More vibrating particles usually mean _____more heat_____.

7. Fewer vibrating particles usually mean _____less heat_____.

8. Temperature is measured in units called _____degrees_____.

9. Heat is measured in units called _____calories_____.

10. Heat makes matter _____expand_____.

MATCHING

Match each term in Column A with its description in Column B. Write the correct letter in the space provided.

	Column A		Column B
__e__	1. temperature	a)	depends upon how fast particles vibrate and how many particles vibrate
__a__	2. heat		
__d__	3. degree	b)	measure of heat
__b__	4. calorie	c)	related but not the same
__c__	5. temperature and heat	d)	measure of temperature
		e)	depends upon how fast particles vibrate

TRUE OR FALSE

In the space provided, write "true" if the sentence is true. Write "false" if the sentence is false.

True   **1.** Heat comes from vibrating particles.

False   **2.** Particles always vibrate at the same speed.

False   **3.** The faster particles vibrate, the less heat they give off.

True   **4.** Temperature tells us how fast particles vibrate.

False   **5.** Temperature is measured in calories.

False   **6.** We measure temperature with a barometer.

False   **7.** Heat depends only on how fast particles vibrate.

True   **8.** Ice has heat.

False   **9.** An ice cube has the same amount of heat as a block of ice.

True   **10.** Heat energy is measured in calories.

REACHING OUT

Is it possible for something small which has a high temperature to have the same amount of heat as something large which has a low temperature?

yes

Lesson **7**

How does a thermometer work?

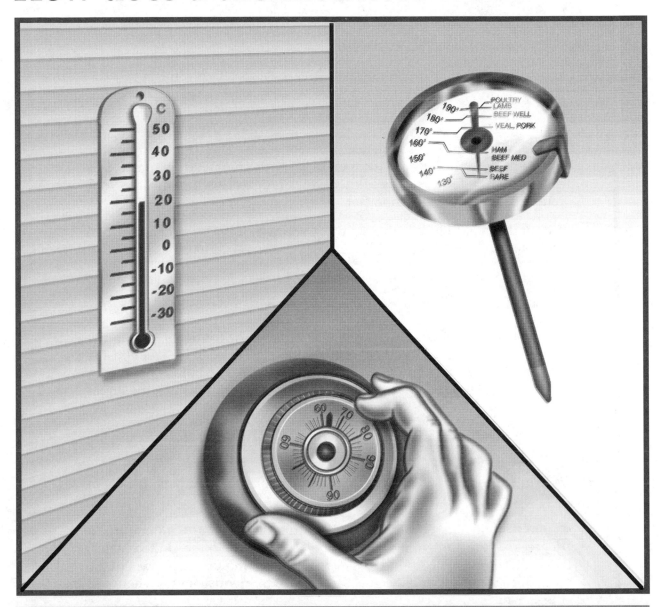

KEY TERMS

Fahrenheit: temperature scale

Celsius: metric temperature scale

LESSON 7 | How does a thermometer work?

Think of all the ways you use thermometers. They tell you indoor temperature and outdoor temperature. A thermometer in meat tells whether your food is done. When you don't feel well, you take your temperature with a thermometer.

No matter what kind of thermometer you use, it works because of two facts you already know:

• Matter expands when it is heated.

• Matter contracts when it is cooled.

In most thermometers the matter that expands or contracts is a liquid. The main part of a thermometer is a long closed tube. At one end the tube gets larger. This closed end is called the bulb. The bulb is filled with a liquid that runs part way up the tube. In most thermometers, the liquid is either mercury or colored alcohol.

• When the liquid in a thermometer is heated, it expands. It rises in the tube.

• When the liquid in the thermometer is cooled, it contracts. It falls in the tube.

Numbers and lines on the side of the tube tell us the temperature in degrees. There are two popular temperature scales. In the United States, the **Fahrenheit** [FER-un-hyt] scale is often used. In most of the rest of the world, the **Celsius** [SEL-see-us] scale is used. Scientists everywhere use the Celsius scale.

STUDYING THERMOMETERS

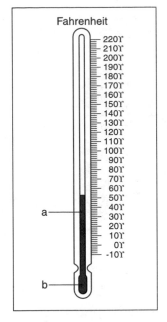

Figure A

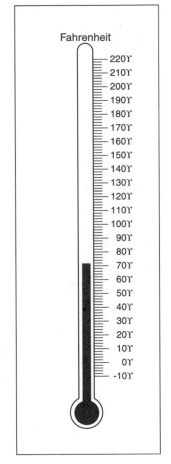

Figure B

Look at the thermometers in Figures A and B. Then answer the questions.

1. The tube is lettered _____a_____ .
   a, b

2. The bulb is lettered _____b_____ .
   a, b

3. Name two liquids that are used in liquid thermometers.
   _____mercury and colored alcohol_____

4. When heated, the liquid _____rises_____ in the tube.
   rises, falls

5. When cooled, the liquid _____falls_____ in the tube.
   rises, falls

6. These are _____Fahrenheit_____ scale thermometers.
   Fahrenheit, Celsius

The temperature on this Fahrenheit thermometer is 72 degrees. In symbol form it is written 72° F.

7. How do you think you write 72 degrees Celsius?
   _____72° C_____

8. In this thermometer, how many degrees does each line stand for? _____two degrees_____

9. Take a guess! Do all thermometers have the same number of degrees between lines? _____no_____

10. Write the following temperatures in symbol form:

    a) twenty-two degrees Fahrenheit _____22° F_____ .

    b) one hundred degrees Celsius _____100° C_____ .

    c) minus five degrees Fahrenheit _____–5° F_____ .

    d) seventy-nine degrees Fahrenheit _____79° F_____ .

    e) forty-four degrees Celsius _____44° C_____ .

Some thermometers tell temperature because a metal coil inside them expands and contracts.

Oven and meat thermometers are examples. So are the thermometers in thermostats.

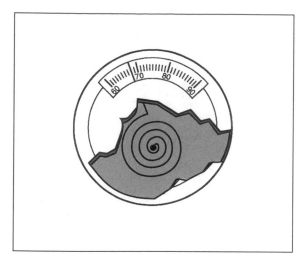

Figure C

FILL IN THE BLANK

Complete each statement using a term or terms from the list below. Write your answers in the spaces provided. Some answers may be used more than once.

become smaller	colored alcohol	become bigger
falls	liquid	heated
Fahrenheit	thermometer	mercury
cooled	rises	Celsius

1. We measure temperature with a ____thermometer____ .

2. A thermometer works because matter expands when ____heated____ and contracts when ____cooled____ .

3. There are two main kinds of temperature scales. They are ____Fahrenheit____ and ____Celsius____ .

4. In science, the ____Celsius____ scale is used most often.

5. Most thermometers contain a ____liquid____ .

6. Two common liquids used in thermometers are ____mercury____ and ____colored alcohol____ .

7. When heated, the liquid ____rises____ in the thermometer tube.

8. When cooled, the liquid ____falls____ in the thermometer tube.

9. Contract means to ____become smaller____ .

10. Expand means to ____become bigger____ .

WORKING WITH THERMOMETERS

The diagram below shows a Fahrenheit thermometer and a Celsius thermometer. See how the scales are different. Study them. Then fill in the temperatures below. Line up the numbers with a straight edge. Each line stands for two degrees.

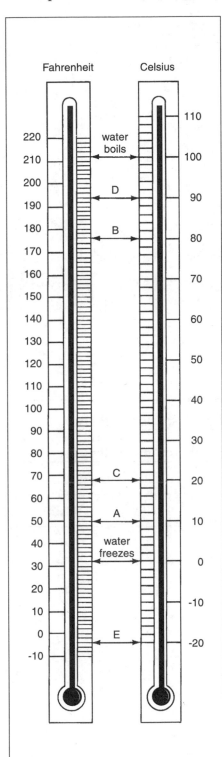

Fill in the missing information in the charts below.

		Fahrenheit	Celsius
1.	Water boils	212°	100°
2.	Water freezes	32°	0°

	Point on Thermometers	Fahrenheit	Celsius
3.	A	50°	10°
4.	B	176°	80°
5.	C	68°	20°
6.	D	194°	90°
7.	E	–4°	–20°

Now answer these questions.

8. 86° F is the same temperature as _____30_____ ° C.

9. 104° F is the same temperature as _____40_____ ° C.

10. 50° C is the same temperature as _____122_____ ° F.

11. –10° C is the same temperature as _____14_____ ° F.

12. 40° C is the same temperature as _____104_____ ° F.

13. 60° C is the same temperature as _____140_____ ° F.

14. 158° F is the same temperature as _____70_____ ° C.

15. What temperature would you want it to be all the time? Write your answer in both Fahrenheit and Celsius.

_____Answers will vary._____ ° F

_____Answers will vary._____ ° C

WORD SEARCH

The list on the left contains words that you have used in this Lesson. Find and circle each word where it appears in the box. The spellings may go in any direction: up, down, left, right, or diagonally.

LIQUID

CALORIE

VIBRATE

DEGREE

MATTER

ABSORB

REFLECT

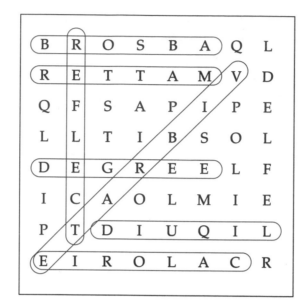

REACHING OUT

Why is water not used in thermometers? Accept all logical responses. Likely responses include that since water freezes at 32° F (0° C), a thermometer that used water could not be used to measure temperatures near freezing.

44

What are compounds?

KEY TERMS

compound: matter made up of two or more different elements

molecule: the smallest part of a compound that has all the properties of that compound, two or more atoms linked together by sharing electrons

formula unit: two or more atoms linked together by transferring electrons, but otherwise similar to a molecule

LESSON 8 | What are compounds?

There are only 26 letters in the alphabet, but you know thousands of words. A good dictionary has hundreds of thousands of words in it. How is this possible?

Words are made up of letters and letters can be put together in many ways. Words can be different lengths. Most words use two or more letters. Some use the same letter more than once. The longest word in the Oxford English Dictionary is FLOCCIPAUCINIHILIPILIFICATION. How many different letters does this word have? How many of these letters are used more than once?

What if you combined the chemical elements? There are more than 110 known elements. But there are probably many more. In fact, there are millions and millions of substances. And new ones are being discovered every day.

Most of the substances we know are made up of two or more elements. Some common examples are water, salt, carbon dioxide, and baking soda. These substances are possible because atoms of different elements can link up.

A **compound** is a substance made of linked-up atoms. The elements in the compound lose their own properties. The compound takes on new properties. Compounds do not even have to be in the same state as the elements of which they are made. For example, hydrogen and oxygen are both gases. They can link up to make water—a liquid. A compound must have at least one metal element and one nonmetal element.

Atoms link up to form compounds in different ways. Sometimes the atoms share electrons and form a molecule. A **molecule** [MAHL-uh-kyool] is the smallest part of a compound that still has the properties of that compound. A molecule has two or more atoms linked together. Some molecules have thousands of atoms.

Other times atoms lend or borrow electrons. When this happens we say the atoms form something called a **formula unit**. Formula units are like molecules. But they differ in how they were put together.

Most compounds are found in nature. Some compounds are made by scientists.

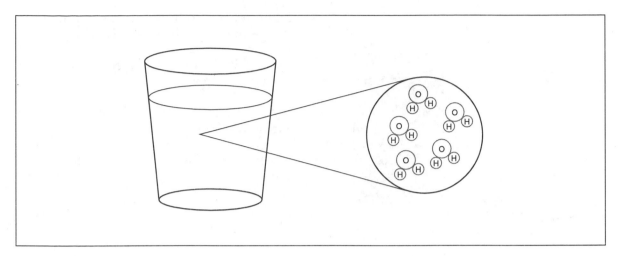

Figure A

Water is a liquid compound. A glass of water has billions and billions of water molecules in it. Each molecule is <u>exactly alike</u>. Each molecule has all of the properties of water. The smallest part of a compound is just <u>one molecule</u> of that compound.

Water is made up of the elements hydrogen and oxygen. Two hydrogen atoms and one oxygen atom combine to make one water molecule.

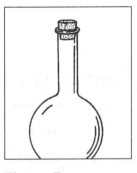

Figure B

Figure C

Figure D

HYDROGEN	+	OXYGEN	→	WATER
invisible gas	+	invisible gas	→	clear liquid
element	+	element	→	compound

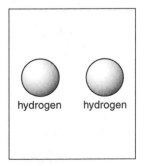

Figure E

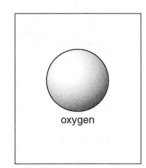

Figure F

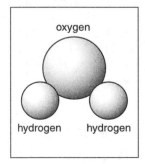

Figure G

SALT

Table salt is a compound. It is made up of the elements sodium and chlorine.

Sodium is a dangerous metal. Chlorine is a poisonous gas.

They can link up to form a compound that our bodies need.

The compound is sodium chloride. We call it <u>salt</u>.

Figure H

SODIUM CHLORIDE

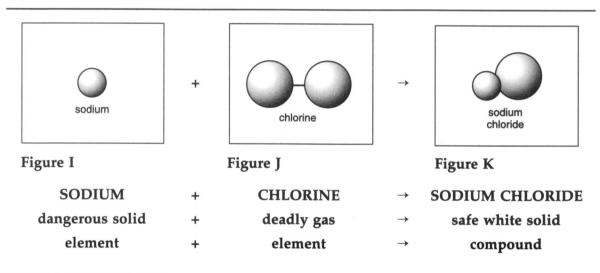

Figure I		**Figure J**		**Figure K**
SODIUM	+	**CHLORINE**	→	**SODIUM CHLORIDE**
dangerous solid	+	**deadly gas**	→	**safe white solid**
element	+	**element**	→	**compound**

CARBON DIOXIDE

<u>Carbon dioxide</u> is a gas compound. It is made of the elements carbon and oxygen.

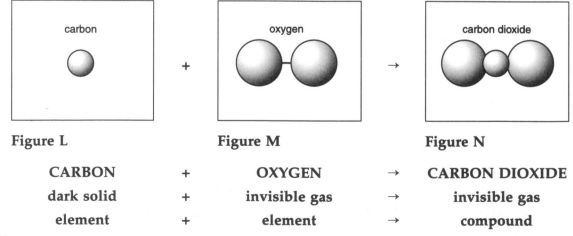

Figure L		**Figure M**		**Figure N**
CARBON	+	**OXYGEN**	→	**CARBON DIOXIDE**
dark solid	+	**invisible gas**	→	**invisible gas**
element	+	**element**	→	**compound**

FILL IN THE BLANK

Complete each statement using a term or terms from the list below. Write your answers in the spaces provided. Some words may be used more than once.

one million	millions	metal	molecule
compounds	110	elements	linked-up
nonmetal	lose	two	formula unit

1. There are more than _____110_____ known elements.

2. The number of different known substances is more than ___one million___ .

3. Elements combine to form ___compounds___ .

4. Elements of a compound _____lose_____ their properties.

5. A compound has at least _____two_____ elements.

6. A compound usually has at least one _____metal_____ atom and one

   _____nonmetal_____ atom.

7. The smallest part of a compound is called a _____molecule_____ or _____formula unit_____ .

8. In a small amount of a compound there may be _____millions_____ of molecules.

9. A compound is made of _____linked-up_____ atoms.

10. All matter is made up of _____elements_____ or ___compounds___ .

MATCHING

Match each term in Column A with its description in Column B. Write the correct letter in the space provided.

	Column A	Column B
__c__ 1.	atom	a) has one kind of atom
__e__ 2.	molecule	b) short way of writing an element
__b__ 3.	symbol	c) smallest part of an element
__a__ 4.	element	d) two or more elements are linked together
__d__ 5.	compound	e) smallest part of a compound
__i__ 6.	water	f) salt
__j__ 7.	carbon dioxide	g) elements that make up salt
__g__ 8.	sodium and chlorine	h) links with a nonmetal
__h__ 9.	metal	i) compound made up of hydrogen and oxygen
__f__ 10.	sodium chloride	j) compound made up of carbon and oxygen

TRUE OR FALSE

In the space provided, write "true" if the sentence is true. Write "false" if the sentence is false.

<u>True</u>   **1.** All matter is made of atoms.

<u>True</u>   **2.** An element is matter.

<u>True</u>   **3.** A compound is matter.

<u>True</u>   **4.** All matter is made of elements or compounds.

<u>True</u>   **5.** Elements and compounds are made of atoms.

<u>False</u>   **6.** Compounds link up to make elements.

<u>False</u>   **7.** A compound can have only one element.

<u>False</u>   **8.** The smallest part of a compound is one atom of that compound.

<u>True</u>   **9.** A compound usually has at least one metal atom and one nonmetal atom.

<u>False</u>   **10.** There are more elements than compounds.

REACHING OUT

Why should you always follow instructions carefully when mixing chemicals?

Accept all logical answers. Likely responses include that if chemicals are not mixed

carefully, dangerous substances may be produced accidentally.

What is a chemical formula?

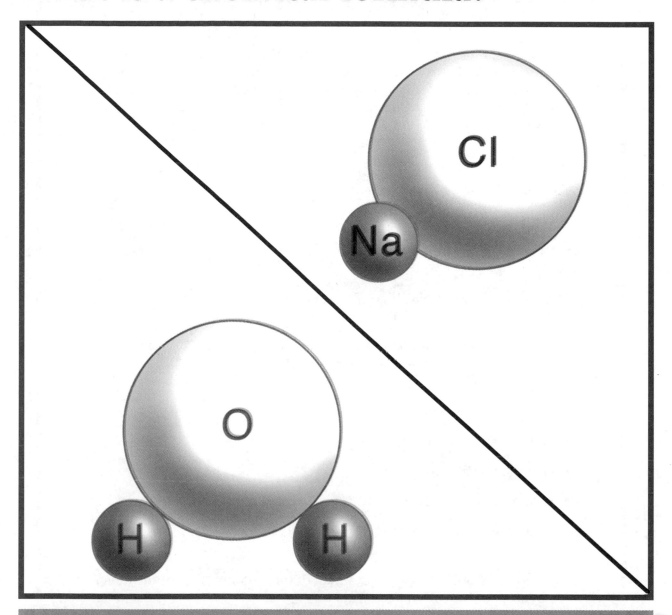

LESSON 9 | What is a chemical formula?

Each element has its own chemical symbol. Each compound has its own **chemical formula**. A formula tells us two important things about a compound. It tells us what elements the compound is made of. It also tells us how many atoms of each element are in a molecule or formula unit of the compound.

The formula for table salt is NaCl.

• Na is the symbol for sodium.

• Cl is the symbol for chlorine.

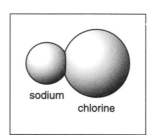
sodium
chlorine

One formula unit of NaCl has a total of two atoms. One of the atoms is sodium (Na). The other atom is chlorine (Cl).

Sometimes a symbol has a small number written next to it. This number tells us the number of atoms there are of that element.

The formula for water is H_2O.

• H is the symbol for hydrogen.

• O is the symbol for oxygen.

• H_2 means two atoms of hydrogen.

• O means one atom of oxygen.

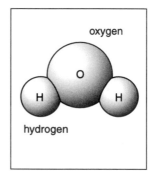
oxygen
O
H   H
hydrogen

One molecule of H_2O, then, has a total of three atoms. Two of the atoms are hydrogen. One atom is oxygen.

The formula for a compound is always the same. A change in the formula means that a new substance was formed.

It is helpful to learn to recognize some chemical symbols. However, if you see one you do not know, you can always look it up in a dictionary, an encyclopedia, or a chemistry book.

SOME COMMON COMPOUNDS

Formula: HgO

Name: mercury (II) oxide

Elements: mercury (Hg) and oxygen (O)

Number of atoms in each element:
      1 atom of mercury (Hg)
      1 atom of oxygen (O)

Total number of atoms in one formula unit:
      2 atoms total

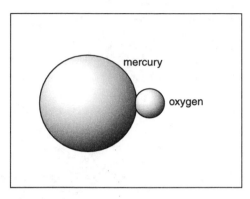

Figure A

Formula: KCl

Name: potassium chloride

Elements: potassium (K) and chlorine (Cl)

Number of atoms in each element:
      1 atom of potassium (K)
      1 atom of chlorine (Cl)

Total number of atoms in one formula unit:
      2 atoms total

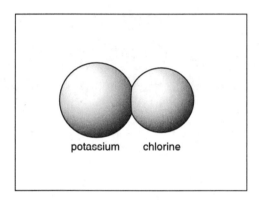

Figure B

Formula: NaOH

Name: sodium hydroxide (lye)

Elements: sodium (Na), oxygen (O), and
      hydrogen (H)

Number of atoms in each element:
      1 atom of sodium (Na)
      1 atom of oxygen (O)
      1 atom of hydrogen (H)

Total number of atoms in one formula unit:
      3 atoms total

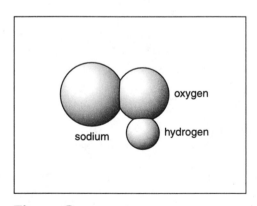

Figure C

MORE COMMON COMPOUNDS

Formula: Fe_2O_3

Name: iron oxide (rust)

Elements: iron (Fe) and oxygen (O)

Number of atoms in each element:
     2 atoms of iron (Fe)
     3 atoms of oxygen (O)

Total number of atoms in one formula unit:
     5 atoms total

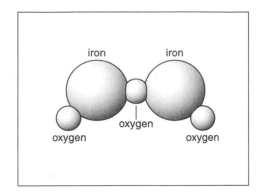

Figure D

Formula: H_2SO_4

Name: sulfuric acid

Elements: hydrogen (H), sulfur (S), and oxygen (O)

Number of atoms in each element:
     2 atoms of hydrogen (H)
     1 atom of sulfur (S)
     4 atoms of oxygen (O)

Total number of atoms in one formula unit:
     7 atoms total

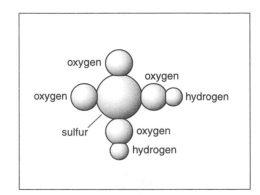

Figure E

Formula: $NaHCO_3$

Name: sodium hydroxide carbonate (baking soda)

Elements: sodium (Na), hydrogen (H), carbon (C), and oxygen (O)

Number of atoms in each element:
     1 atom of sodium (Na)
     1 atom of hydrogen (H)
     1 atom of carbon (C)
     3 atoms of oxygen (O)

Total number of atoms in one formula unit:
     6 atoms total

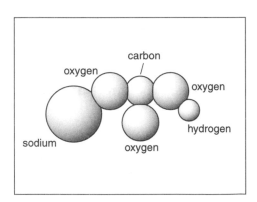

Figure F

COMPLETING SENTENCES

Choose the correct word or term for each statement. Write your choice in the spaces provided.

1. A molecule is made up of _____atoms_____ .
   <small>atoms, oxygen</small>

2. A single molecule has at least _____two_____ atoms.
   <small>one, two</small>

3. _____Elements_____ are combined to make _____compounds_____ .
   <small>Elements, Compounds</small>   <small>elements, compounds</small>

4. There are _____fewer_____ elements than compounds.
   <small>more, fewer</small>

5. Molecules are usually _____larger_____ than atoms.
   <small>larger, smaller</small>

The formula for starch is $C_6H_{10}O_5$. This stands for one molecule of starch. Answer these questions about the starch molecule.

6. Starch is made up of _____three_____ elements.
   <small>one, two, three</small>

7. The number of different <u>kinds</u> of atoms in starch is _____three_____ .
   <small>three, billions</small>

8. One molecule of starch has _____ten_____ atoms of hydrogen.
   <small>two, six, ten</small>

9. The total number of atoms in one molecule of starch is _____21_____ .
   <small>6, 10, 16, 21</small>

10. The number of molecules in a teaspoon of starch is _____more than a billion_____ .
    <small>about one hundred, more than a billion</small>

MATCHING

Match each term in Column A with its description in Column B. Write the correct letter in the space provided.

	Column A		Column B
b	1. CaF_2	a)	contains one kind of atom
c	2. HF	b)	3 atoms in each formula unit
e	3. formula	c)	2 atoms in each formula unit
a	4. element	d)	short way of writing an element
d	5. symbol	e)	short way of writing a compound

COMPLETE THE CHART

Complete the chart by filling in the missing information. The first one has been done for you.

Formula	Name	Number of Elements	Names of the Elements	Number of Atoms of Each Element	Total Number of Atoms In One Formula Unit
1. MgO	magnesium oxide	2	magnesium oxygen	1 1	2
2. SO_2	sulfur dioxide	2	sulfur oxygen	1 2	3
3. NH_3	ammonia	2	nitrogen hydrogen	1 3	4
4. H_2CO_3	carbonic acid (soda water)	3	hydrogen carbon oxygen	2 1 3	6
5. $C_{12}H_{22}O_{11}$	table sugar	3	carbon hydrogen oxygen	12 22 11	45
6. $MgSO_4$	magnesium sulfate (Epsom salts)	3	magnesium sulfur oxygen	1 1 4	6
7. $NaOH$	sodium hydroxide (lye)	3	sodium oxygen hydrogen	1 1 1	3
8. H_2O_2	hydrogen peroxide	2	hydrogen oxygen	2 2	4
9. Fe_2O_3	iron oxide (rust)	2	iron oxygen	2 3	5
10. $NaHCO_3$	sodium bicarbonate (baking soda)	4	sodium hydrogen carbon oxygen	1 1 1 3	6

Lesson **10**

How do elements form compounds?

KEY TERMS

shells: energy levels in which electrons are arranged around the nucleus

stable: is not likely to change, prefers to stay the way it is

borrow: to use something that belongs to someone or something else

lend: to let someone use something that belongs to you

inert gases (noble gases): elements which have complete outer electron shells, gases which rarely react with other elements

LESSON 10 | How do elements form compounds?

You know that the electrons in atoms orbit the nucleus. You also know that electrons are arranged in **shells** around the nucleus.

What you probably did not know (but soon will) is that atoms "want" to have two or eight electrons in their outermost shells. Atoms with two or eight electrons in their outermost shells are more **stable** than atoms with some other number of electrons in their outermost shell.

In order to have a stable outermost electron shell, atoms can share electrons. Atoms that do this form molecules. Atoms can also lend or borrow electrons. Atoms that do this form something called formula units. One atom **borrows** electrons from another atom. The second atom **lends** its electrons to the first atom. This is how elements combine to form compounds.

Metals usually have less than four electrons in their outermost shell. Nonmetals usually have more than four electrons in their outermost shell. Metals lend electrons to nonmetals. Nonmetals borrow electrons from metals.

For example, sodium has one electron in its outermost shell (M shell). Chlorine has seven electrons in its outermost shell (M shell). Sodium and chlorine can combine to form sodium chloride. The sodium atom lends the only electron in its M shell to the chlorine atom. Sodium now has eight electrons in its outermost shell (now the L shell), and chlorine has eight electrons in its outermost shell (still the M shell).

Some atoms that already have complete outer shells do not easily combine with any other atoms. Also, just because an atom can combine with another atom does not mean that it will combine with the other atom.

FORMING SODIUM CHLORIDE

Sodium and chlorine combine to form sodium chloride.

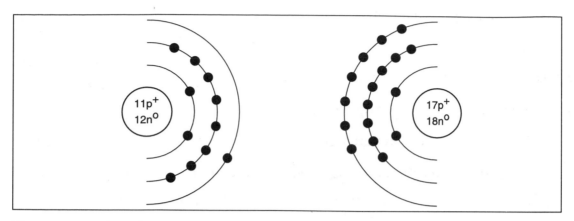

Figure A *Sodium has one electron in its outermost shell (M shell) and chlorine has seven electrons in its outermost shell (M shell).*

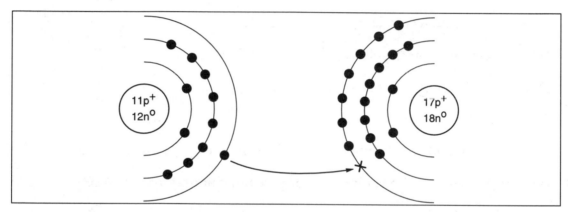

Figure B *The sodium atom lends the only electron in its M shell to the chlorine atom.*

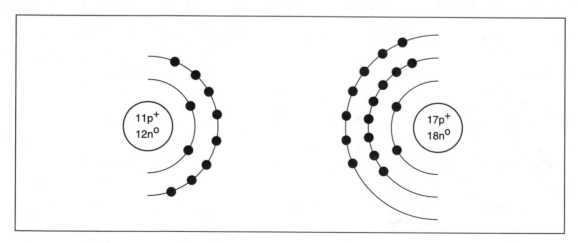

Figure C *Sodium now has eight electrons in its outermost shell (now the L shell), and chlorine has eight electrons in its outermost shell (still the M shell).*

Now answer the following questions.

1. How many outer-ring electrons does sodium have? _____1_____

2. Is sodium's outer shell complete? _____no_____

3. Is sodium a metal or a nonmetal? _____metal_____

4. How many outer-ring electrons does chlorine have? _____7_____

5. Is chlorine's outer shell complete? _____no_____

6. Is chlorine a metal or a nonmetal? _____nonmetal_____

7. Altogether, how many outer-ring electrons do sodium and chlorine have? (Count them.) _____8_____

8. Together, can they make a complete shell? _____yes_____

9. Which atom is the electron "lender"? _____sodium_____

10. How many electrons are lent? _____1_____

11. Which atom borrows the electron? _____chlorine_____

12. How many electrons are borrowed? _____1_____

13. Do they make a compound? _____yes_____

14. When sodium and chlorine link up, do their properties change? _____yes_____

15. What is the name of the compound sodium and chlorine make? _____sodium chloride_____

COMPLETING SENTENCES

Choose the correct word or term for each statement. Write your choice in the spaces provided.

1. The outer ring of a metal has _____fewer_____ than four electrons.

fewer, more

2. Metals _____lend_____ electrons.

lend, borrow

3. The outer ring of a nonmetal has _____more_____ than four electrons.

fewer, more

4. Nonmetals _____borrow_____ electrons.

lend, borrow

5. Most elements are _____metals_____ .

metals, nonmetals

FORMING CALCIUM OXIDE

Calcium and oxygen join to form the compound calcium oxide (CaO).

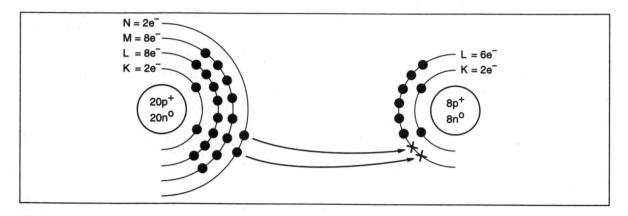

Figure D

Answer the following questions.

1. How many outer-ring electrons does calcium have? _____2_____

2. Is this a complete shell? _____no_____

3. Is calcium a metal or nonmetal? _____metal_____

4. How many outer-ring electrons does oxygen have? _____6_____

5. Is this a complete shell? _____no_____

6. Is oxygen a metal or a nonmetal? _____nonmetal_____

7. Altogether, how many outer-ring electrons do calcium and oxygen have? (Count them.) _____8_____

8. Together, can they make a complete shell? _____yes_____

9. Which atom lends electrons? _____calcium_____

10. How many electrons are lent? _____2_____

11. Which atom borrows the electrons? _____oxygen_____

12. How many electrons are borrowed? _____2_____

13. Do they form a compound? _____yes_____

14. When calcium and oxygen link up, do their properties change? _____yes_____

15. What is the name of the compound oxygen and calcium form? _____calcium oxide_____

COMPLETE THE CHART

Complete the chart by filling in the missing information. The first has been done for you.

Element	Number of Electrons in Outer Ring	Metal or Nonmetal?	Electron Lender or Borrower?	Lends or Borrows How Many Electrons?
1. calcium	2	metal	lender	2
2. sodium	1	metal	lender	1
3. phosphorus	5	nonmetal	borrower	3
4. potassium	1	metal	lender	1
5. oxygen	6	nonmetal	borrower	2
6. iodine	7	nonmetal	borrower	1
7. cesium	1	metal	lender	1
8. bromine	7	nonmetal	borrower	1
9. sulfur	6	nonmetal	borrower	2
10. magnesium	2	metal	lender	2

TRUE OR FALSE

In the space provided, write "true" if the sentence is true. Write "false" if the sentence is false.

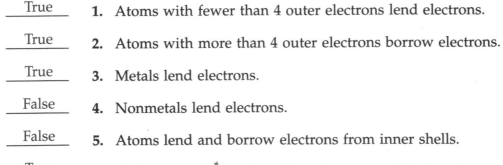

True	1.	Atoms with fewer than 4 outer electrons lend electrons.
True	2.	Atoms with more than 4 outer electrons borrow electrons.
True	3.	Metals lend electrons.
False	4.	Nonmetals lend electrons.
False	5.	Atoms lend and borrow electrons from inner shells.
True	6.	Only outer shells gain or lose electrons with other atoms.
False	7.	All atoms form compounds.
False	8.	Every element can link up with every other element.
False	9.	Atoms with more than 4 outer electrons are metals.
True	10.	Atoms with more than 4 outer electrons are nonmetals.

COMPLETE THE CHART

Complete the chart by filling in the missing information. The first has been done for you.

The elements in Group 18 do not lend or borrow electrons because their outer electron shell is naturally complete. They are often called **noble gases** or **inert gases** because they do not usually combine with other elements.

Elements of Group	Lend Electrons?	Borrow Electrons?	Metal or Nonmetal?
1	Yes	No	metal
2	Yes	No	metal
13	Yes	No	metal
15	No	Yes	nonmetal
16	No	Yes	nonmetal
17	No	Yes	nonmetal
18	No	No	nonmetal

MATCHING

Match each term in Column A with its description in Column B. Write the correct letter in the space provided.

Column A

_e_ 1. metals

_c_ 2. two or eight

_b_ 3. sodium and chlorine

_a_ 4. hydrogen and oxygen

_d_ 5. nonmetals

Column B

a) link up to form water

b) link up to form salt

c) number of electrons in a complete outer ring

d) borrow electrons

e) lend electrons

Calcium and chlorine link up to form calcium chloride. Look at the diagrams of these atoms. Fill in the missing parts on each diagram. Then answer the questions.

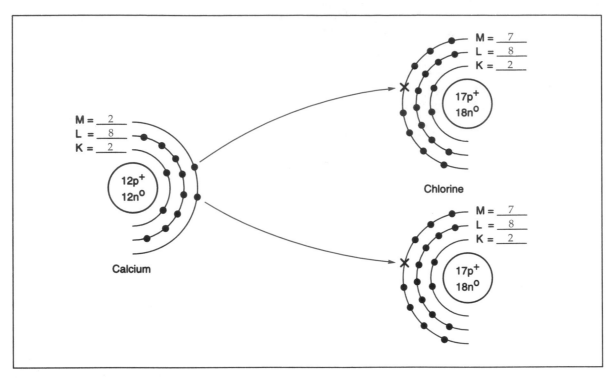

Figure E

1. How many outer-ring electrons does a calcium atom have? _____2_____

2. How many outer-ring electrons does a chlorine atom have? _____7_____

3. Which atom lends electrons? _____calcium_____

4. How many electrons does <u>one</u> atom of this element lend? _____2_____

5. Which atom borrows electrons? _____chlorine_____

6. How many electrons does <u>one</u> atom of this element borrow? _____1_____

7. How many chlorine atoms are needed to link up with <u>one</u> calcium atom? Explain.

   Two chlorine atoms are needed. Calcium has two electrons to lend.

   Each chlorine atom can borrow only one electron. Therefore, two chlorine atoms

   are needed.

8. What is the formula for calcium chloride? _____$CaCl_2$_____

What is the difference between a physical change and a chemical change?

KEY TERMS

physical change: a change in matter that does not produce any new products or substances

chemical change: change in matter that produces new substances

chemical reaction: process involving a chemical change

LESSON 11 | What is the difference between a physical change and a chemical change?

There are different ways you can change things. For example, you can tear up a piece of paper into small pieces. What remains is still paper. You have changed the way the paper looks. But you have not made any new substance. You have made a physical change.

If, instead, you burned the paper, what would be left? What is left is no longer paper. In this case the substance has been changed. This is a chemical change.

A **physical change** does not change the way the atoms are linked up. The substance may look different, but no new substance has been formed. The chemical properties are not changed.

In a physical change, no energy is taken in or given off <u>unless</u> there is a change of state.

In a **chemical change**, matter changes from one kind of material to another kind of material. The atoms that make up the material <u>do not</u> change. Instead, the atoms change the way they are linked up. The new substances can have very different properties than the old substances.

Chemical changes take place during chemical reactions. In a **chemical reaction** there is never a change in the number of elements. There is never a change in the number of atoms of one element. No elements are lost. No new elements are added. They just combine in different ways.

Energy is always part of a chemical reaction. In a chemical reaction, energy is either taken in or given off.

Electrolysis is an example of a <u>chemical change</u>. Electrical energy is used to break water molecules apart into oxygen and hydrogen. Figure B shows a diagram of the chemical reaction taking place during electrolysis. The molecules on the <u>left</u> side of the arrow were present before the electrolysis took place. The molecules on the <u>right</u> side of the arrow were present <u>after</u> the electrolysis took place. Look at the diagram and then answer the question below.

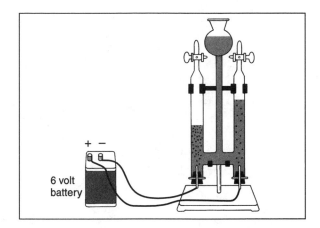

Figure A

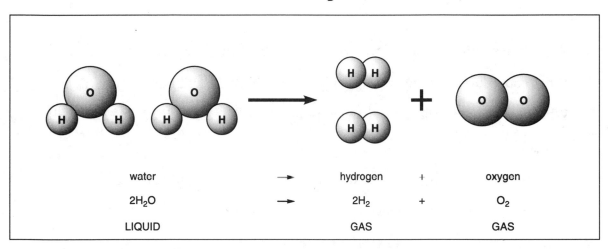

water	→	hydrogen	+	oxygen
$2H_2O$	→	$2H_2$	+	O_2
LIQUID		GAS		GAS

Figure B

1. What compound did we start with? _____water_____

2. What two elements make up that compound? ___hydrogen___ ___oxygen___

3. What two elements did we end up with? ___hydrogen___ ___oxygen___

4. Were new substances formed? _____yes_____

5. Are the properties of the old and new substances different? _____yes_____

6. How many atoms of hydrogen did we start with? _____4_____

7. How many atoms of oxygen did we start with? _____2_____

8. How many atoms of hydrogen did we end up with? _____4_____

9. How many atoms of oxygen did we end up with? _____2_____

10. Did the type and number of atoms change? _____no_____

11. Does electrolysis cause a chemical change or physical change? ___chemical change___

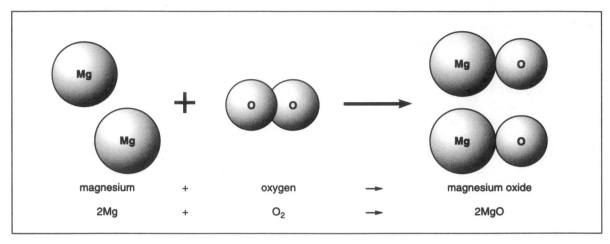

magnesium   +   oxygen   →   magnesium oxide

$2Mg$ + O_2 → $2MgO$

Figure C

1. What two elements did we start with? <u>magnesium</u> <u>oxygen</u>

2. What compound did we end up with? <u>magnesium oxide</u>

3. What two elements make up that compound? <u>magnesium</u> <u>oxygen</u>

4. Was a new substance formed? <u>yes</u>

5. Are the properties of the old and new substances different? <u>yes</u>

6. How many atoms of magnesium did we start with? <u>2</u>

7. How many atoms of oxygen did we start with? <u>2</u>

8. How many atoms of magnesium did we end up with? <u>2</u>

9. How many atoms of oxygen did we end up with? <u>2</u>

10. Did the type and number of atoms change? <u>no</u>

11. Does burning magnesium cause a chemical change or physical change? <u>a chemical change</u>

SHREDDING PAPER

Shredding paper is an example of a physical change. In a physical change, the atoms do not change the way they are linked up. No new products are formed. Look at Figure F and then answer the questions below.

Figure F

1. Does the paper look different after being shredded? _____yes_____

2. Is the paper still paper? _____yes_____

3. Are the atoms taking in energy? _____no_____

4. Are the atoms giving off energy? _____no_____

5. In a physical change, the atoms _____do not_____ change the way they link up.
   do, do not

6. The chemical properties of the paper _____are not_____ changed.
   are, are not

Figure G

Melting ice is an example of a change of state. A solid (ice) changes into a liquid (water). The formula for water is H_2O. The formula for ice also is H_2O. Both ice and water have the same chemical formula. Therefore no chemical change takes place. A change of state (such as melting ice) is a physical change.

Energy is taken in when ice melts. Changes of state are the only physical changes where energy is taken in or given off. Look at Figure G and then answer the questions below.

1. Does the ice look different after it melts? _____ yes _____

2. When ice changes to water, the link-up of the atoms _____ does not _____ change.
   does, does not

3. When water changes to ice, the link-up of the atoms _____ does not _____ change.
   does, does not

4. The melting of ice is an example of a _____ physical _____ change.
   physical, chemical

5. When ice changes to a liquid, the ice _____ does _____ take in energy.
   does, does not

6. Usually, energy _____ is not _____ part of a physical change.
   is, is not

7. Energy is part of a physical change only when there is _____ a change of state _____ .
   electrolysis, a change of state

Figure H

Look at Figure H and then answer the questions below.

1. Does the wood look different after being chopped? _____ yes _____

2. Is the wood still wood? _____ yes _____

3. Have the atoms changed the way they are linked up? _____ no _____

4. Have any elements been added? _____ no _____

5. Have any elements been lost? _____ no _____

6. Were any new products formed? _____ no _____

7. Did the wood take in energy? _____ no _____

8. Did the wood give off energy? _____ no _____

9. The chopping of wood is an example of a _____ physical _____ change.
   physical, chemical

10. What is the difference between a physical change and a chemical change?

    In a chemical change, the way the atoms link up is changed; in a physical change,

    the atoms do not link up any differently.

TRUE OR FALSE

In the space provided, write "true" if the sentence is true. Write "false" if the sentence is false.

True   **1.** A chemical reaction causes a chemical change.

True   **2.** A chemical change makes new products.

False   **3.** Elements can be lost or gained in a chemical reaction.

False   **4.** Energy can be taken in only during a chemical reaction.

False   **5.** The substances that take part in a chemical reaction keep their properties.

True   **6.** The new substances made in a chemical reaction have new properties.

False   **7.** A physical change makes new products.

False   **8.** The boiling of water is an example of a chemical change.

True   **9.** The electrolysis of water is an example of a chemical change.

True   **10.** Some physical changes involve taking in or giving off energy.

CHEMICAL CHANGE OR PHYSICAL CHANGE?

Tell whether each of the following is a chemical change or a physical change.

1. mixing salt and pepper   physical change

2. evaporation of water   physical change

3. electrolysis of water   chemical change

4. cutting a marshmallow   physical change

5. toasting a marshmallow   chemical change

6. burning magnesium   chemical change

7. demolishing a car   physical change

8. the rusting of iron   chemical change

9. melting of sugar   physical change

10. baking a cake   chemical change

72

Lesson **12**

How is a mixture different from a compound?

KEY TERM

mixture: two or more substances that are physically combined

LESSON 12 | How is a mixture different from a compound?

Sometimes two or more substances are just mixed together. They do not combine chemically. They do not make a compound. They make a **mixture**. The substances are physically combined. None of the substances in the mixture have been changed chemically. No chemical reaction has taken place. No new substances are formed.

Vegetable soup is an example of a mixture. So is salt and sand mixed together. You can still tell one part from the other.

What are the differences between a compound and a mixture? The chart below lists some of the differences.

MIXTURE	COMPOUND
The parts of a mixture do not change their properties.	The elements that make up a compound lose their chemical properties. The new compound has its own chemical properties.
The ratio between the parts of a mixture may be any amount.	The ratio between the parts of a mixture is a fixed amount.
Energy is not taken in or given off when a mixture is made or separated.	Energy is always taken in or given off when a compound is broken up or put together.
A mixture can be separated by physical means. For example, a strainer can separate some mixtures.	A compound can be separated only with a chemical reaction. For example, electrolysis changes water (H_2O) into hydrogen and oxygen.

ABOUT MIXTURES

A mixture can have many kinds of matter. It can have:

elements only　　　or　　　compounds only　　　or　　elements and compounds

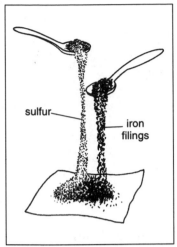

Figure A

Figure B

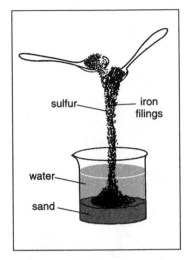

Figure C

SALT AND PEPPER

Salt mixed with pepper is an example of a mixture. The salt and pepper are just close together. They do not react together. Properties do not change. The salt is still salt. The pepper is still pepper. No new products are formed.

It makes no difference how much pepper or salt there is. No exact amounts are needed. Energy is not taken in or given off by the molecules of the salt or the pepper.

Figure D

Salt is a compound. Pepper is a compound. Salt with pepper is a mixture made up of two compounds.

TRUE OR FALSE

In the space provided, write "true" if the sentence is true. Write "false" if the sentence is false.

    False   **1.** A ratio of the parts of a mixture are exact.

    True   **2.** A ratio of the parts of a compound are exact.

    True   **3.** The parts of a mixture keep their properties.

    False   **4.** The elements of a compound keep their properties.

    True   **5.** We need energy to make or break up a compound.

    False   **6.** Hydrogen is a compound.

    True   **7.** Water is a compound.

    True   **8.** We need a chemical reaction to separate a compound.

    True   **9.** Electricity can separate some compounds.

    False   **10.** A magnet can separate water into oxygen and hydrogen.

MAKING A MIXTURE AND A COMPOUND

PART I   Making a Mixture

What You Need (Materials)

measuring cup
  (which has never been used
  in a lab before)
teaspoon
water
table salt

table salt
measuring cup
water

Figure E

Figure F

How to Do the Experiment (Procedure)

Make sure your hands are clean before you do this experiment.

1. Fill the measuring cup with a half cup of water.

   Note: Make sure the measuring cup has never been used in a lab before and has never had any dangerous chemical in it.

2. Add about 2 teaspoons of table salt to the water (Figure E).

3. Mix them together (Figure F).

4. Taste a little bit of the mixture.

What You Learned (Observations)

1. How did the mixture taste? _____salty_____

2. What did the mixture look like? _____water_____

3. How do you think you could separate the salt from the water?

   _____Answers may include heating it or letting the water evaporate._____

Something to Think About (Conclusions)

1. Did the properties of the salt change? _____no_____

2. Did the properties of the water change? _____no_____

3. Was a new product formed? _____no_____

4. Did a chemical reaction take place? _____no_____

5. Salt and water together make a _____mixture_____ .

6. There _____was not_____ a chemical change.
   was, was not

PART II Making a Compound

What You Need (Materials)

6-volt lantern battery
two pieces of insulated wire (about 10" long)
  with 1" of insulation removed from both ends
two large steel nails
small jar (big enough to hold the nails)
saltwater mixture from Part I

Note: Do not use household current. Use only the battery. Do not let any flame get near your work area.

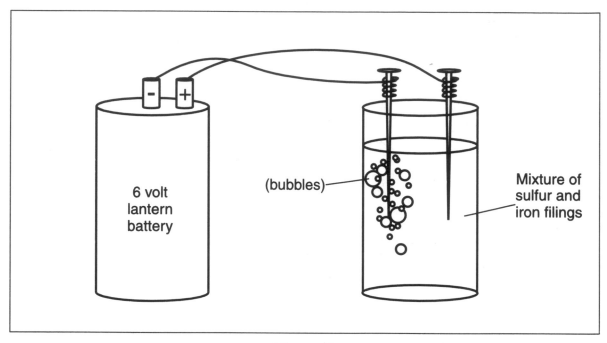

Figure G

How to Do the Experiment (Procedure)

1. Fill the small jar with the saltwater mixture from Part I.

2. Connect one wire to the negative terminal of the battery. Wrap the other end around one of the nails.

3. Connect the other wire to the positive terminal of the battery. Wrap the other end around the other nail.

4. Place both nails in the salt water. They should be close but not touching.

5. If you do not see bubbles near the nail attached to the negative terminal, check your connections and your battery.

6. Let the electricity flow for about five minutes.

7. Disconnect the wires from the battery and remove the nails from the water.

What You Learned (Observations)

1. What did the mixture look like at the start of the experiment? <u>It was colorless.</u>

2. How did the mixture change during the experiment? <u>It changed colors.</u>

3. What else did you notice in the jar? <u>Small solid particles formed.</u>

4. Did the properties of the mixture change? <u>yes</u>

Something to Think About (Conclusions)

1. Was a new product formed? <u>yes</u>

2. Did a chemical reaction take place? <u>yes</u>

3. An electric current flowing through iron nails in a saltwater mixture makes a

    <u>compound</u> .
    mixture, compound

4. The iron nails gave off electrons. The hydroxide (OH) part of the water molecule

    probably took them on. Take a guess—the particles formed in this experiment are

    called <u>iron hydroxide</u> .

MIXTURE OR COMPOUND

The chart below lists some terms and phrases that describe mixtures and compounds. Which ones describe mixtures? Which describe compounds? Put a check (✔) in the space to show your choice.

		Mixture	Compound
1.	properties change		✔
2.	properties do not change	✔	
3.	exact ratios of elements		✔
4.	no exact ratios of elements	✔	
5.	energy always taken in or given off		✔
6.	energy not taken in or given off	✔	
7.	separated by chemical means		✔
8.	separated by physical means	✔	
9.	a pile of iron filings and sulfur	✔	
10.	iron sulfide		✔

SCIENCE *EXTRA*

Buckyballs

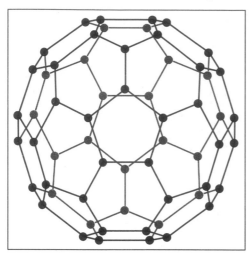

Atoms can form molecules in a number of ways. Scientists are always trying to discover new ways that atoms bond together. In 1985, Richard Smalley and Harold Kroto were seeing what types of molecules would form when they heated carbon atoms to 8,000°C (14,500°F). They discovered something remarkable—a new form of carbon.

Before this discovery, scientists knew of only two types of molecules that carbon atoms could form, graphite and diamonds. Graphite is made up of layers of carbon atoms. Graphite is found in pencils and is often incorrectly called "pencil lead." Diamonds are also made up of pure carbon. The carbon atoms in diamonds are arranged in an octohedral (eight sided) form. This structure makes diamonds very strong.

Naturally, Smalley and Kroto were very excited when they discovered a third form of carbon. What was the shape of this new molecule? The chemists ran some tests and discovered two things—the new molecule has sixty atoms and the molecule had no "edges." An "edge" is a place on

a molecule for other atoms or molecules to link onto easily.

The shape that fit this description was a sphere, or more exactly, a geodesic [jee-uh-DES-ik] dome. In honor of Buckminster Fuller, the inventor of the geodesic dome, the new molecules are called buckyballs.

Because buckyballs are round, they spin very, very fast — up to a billion times a second! This makes it impossible to use powerful microscopes to take pictures of buckyballs. Without a picture of a buckyball, no one could prove that they were really shaped like a geodesic dome.

That was until Joel Hawkins and a group of chemists from the University of California at Berkeley developed a method of "grabbing" a buckyball by attaching it to another molecule. This stopped the buckyball from spinning so that a picture could be taken.

Now that the existence of buckyballs has been confirmed, scientists are working even harder to discover ways to make use of it. After all, it's not every day that a new form of carbon is discovered.

How can mixtures be separated?

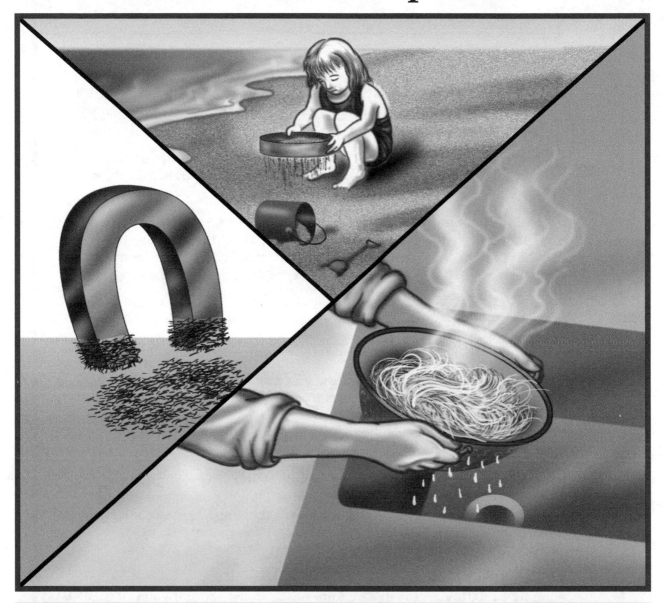

KEY TERMS

dissolve: to make a solid matter disappear in a liquid

evaporate: change from a liquid to a gas

LESSON 13 | How can mixtures be separated?

When you separate a mixture, you just separate the parts. You do not separate the linked-up atoms. Mixtures are separated without any chemical reaction.

There are many different kinds of mixtures. Different mixtures are separated in different ways. There are four main ways to separate a mixture. They are:

STRAINING   Straining separates matter by size. A strainer has holes. Any matter that is smaller than the holes passes through the holes. Anything larger than the holes stays in the strainer. Strainers come in different sizes—some have large holes, some have small holes.

Filter paper is a kind of strainer. Filter paper has very tiny holes. It separates tiny pieces of solids from the liquids they are mixed with.

USING A MAGNET   A magnet separates iron parts from a mixture.

EVAPORATION   When some substances mix with water, they seem to disappear. Think of sugar and water. In water, sugar seems to disappear. The sugar **dissolves**. Solids can be dissolved in other liquids as well. However, not all solids can be dissolved. Think of sand in water. Does sand dissolve in water?

Sugar and water form a mixture, <u>not</u> a compound. The sugar molecules do not change. You can taste the sugar even though you cannot see it. If you let the water evaporate, the sugar will remain. The sugar will <u>not</u> evaporate. Mixtures like sugar and water can be separated using evaporation. A liquid will **evaporate** [i-VAP-uh-rayt] faster if you heat it.

DISSOLVING   Dissolving is sometimes helpful when you want to separate a mixture. Think of a mixture of sugar and sand. If you put this mixture in water, the sugar will dissolve. The sand will not dissolve. Now you can filter out the sand from the water. Then, you can evaporate the water leaving the sugar behind.

WHAT DO THE PICTURES SHOW?

Five of the pictures below show a mixture being separated. The other picture shows a step needed before separation can be done.

Look at each picture. Then answer the questions on the next page. Write the letter of the right picture for each question.

Figure A

Figure B

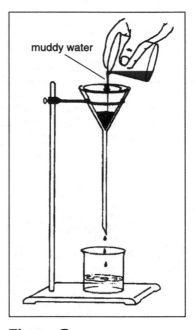

Figure C

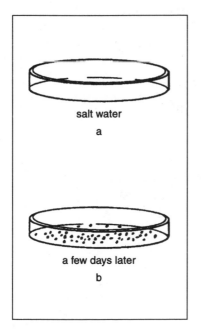

Figure D

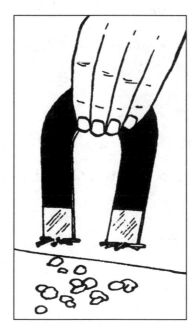

Figure E

Figure F

1. Which pictures show straining? ___B___ ___C___ ___F___

2. Which picture shows filter paper being used? ___C___

3. Which picture shows pieces of iron being separated? ___E___

4. Which pictures show dissolving? ___A___

5. Which picture shows evaporation? ___D___

FILL IN THE BLANK

Complete each statement using a term or terms from the list below. Write your answers in the spaces provided. Some words may be used more than once.

mixture	straining	iron
air	size	using a magnet
dissolving	dissolve	strainer
evaporation	filter paper	holes
heated		

1. Four ways to separate mixtures are: ___straining___, ___using a magnet___,

    ___evaporation___ , and ___dissolving___ .

2. Straining separates matter according to ___size___ .

3. A ___strainer___ separates matter by size.

4. A strainer has many ___holes___ .

5. We can separate a mixture of very tiny solid pieces and water by using

    ___filter paper___ .

6. We use a magnet to separate ___iron___ from a mixture.

7. When water evaporates, the vapor escapes into the ___air___ .

8. A solid that seems to disappear in a liquid is said to ___dissolve___ .

9. Sugar and water are a ___mixture___ .

10. A liquid will evaporate faster if it is ___heated___ .

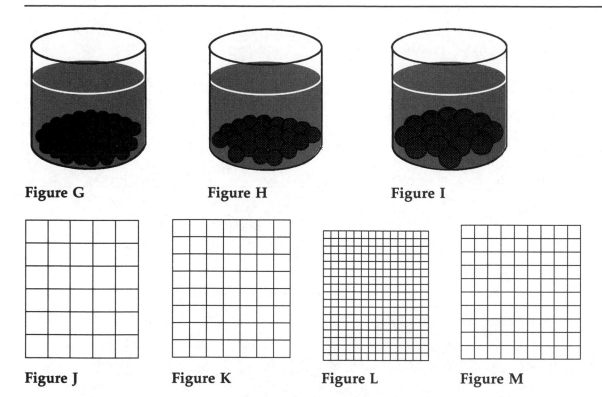

Figure G   **Figure H**   **Figure I**

Figure J   **Figure K**   **Figure L**   **Figure M**

Figures G, H, and I each show a glass of water with marbles in it. Figures J, K, L, and M each show a screen strainer. Using a metric ruler, measure the marbles in each glass. Then measure the size of one of the openings in each strainer. Complete each of the statements below using the term or terms from the list below.

strainer J	strainer L	3 mm	4 mm	5 mm
strainer K	2 mm	3.5 mm	4.5 mm	6 mm

1. The marbles in Figure G measure _____3 mm_____ across.

2. The marbles in Figure H measure _____4 mm_____ across.

3. The marbles in Figure I measure _____5 mm_____ across.

4. The openings in Figure J measure _____6 mm_____ across.

5. The openings in Figure K measure _____4.5 mm_____ across.

6. The openings in Figure L measure _____2 mm_____ across.

7. The openings in Figure M measure _____3.5 mm_____ across.

8. _____Strainer L_____ will separate all the shown solids from the water.

9. _____Strainer J_____ will separate none of the shown solids from the water.

10. _____Strainer M_____ is the largest strainer that can separate the solids in glass H.

WORD SCRAMBLE

Below are several scrambled words you have used in this Lesson. Unscramble the words and write your answers in the spaces provided.

1. VISOLEDS   DISSOLVE

2. AVOPEATER   EVAPORATE

3. TIREXUM   MIXTURE

4. MONDOCUP   COMPOUND

5. TAGMEN   MAGNET

TRUE OR FALSE

In the space provided, write "true" if the sentence is true. Write "false" if the sentence is false.

False   1. Straining causes a chemical change.

False   2. Evaporation causes a chemical change.

True   3. A magnet causes a physical change.

True   4. Dissolving causes a physical change.

False   5. Filter paper has large holes.

False   6. Only scientists use strainers.

True   7. When a liquid evaporates, its molecules go into the air.

True   8. Sugar dissolved in water is still sugar.

True   9. A magnet can separate a mixture of paper clips and rubber bands.

True   10. Hot water evaporates faster than cold water.

HOW WOULD YOU SEPARATE THESE MIXTURES?

Five kinds of mixtures are listed below. Can you decide how to separate these mixtures? Before making up your mind, study the diagrams. Each diagram shows a different step used in separating mixtures.

Mixture 1   salt and iron filings
Mixture 2   salty water
Mixture 3   salt, iron filings, and water
Mixture 4   gravel, sand, and sugar
Mixture 5   gravel, sand, sugar, and iron filings

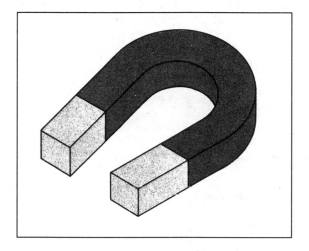

Figure N   *A magnet is used to separate iron.*

Figure O   *Water is used to dissolve a solid.*

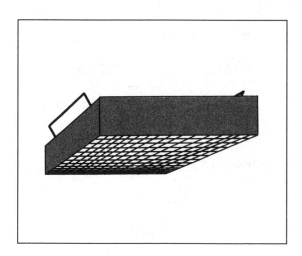

Figure P   *A strainer is used to separate large solids.*

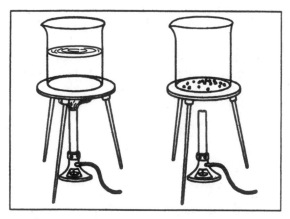

Figure Q *Evaporation is used to separate already dissolved solids.*

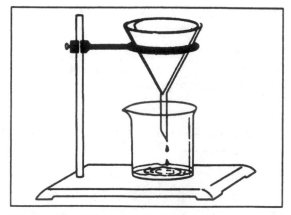

Figure R *Filtration is used to separate very small solids.*

Now decide which step or steps are needed to separate mixtures 1 through 5. In the blank spaces below, write down the steps you would use. In most cases, the order in which the steps are taken is not important.

Mixture 1: salt and iron filings (only one step is needed)

Step 1: A magnet is used to separate the iron filings

Mixture 2: salt water (only one step is needed)

Step 1: Evaporation is used to separate already dissolved solids

Mixture 3: salt, iron filings, and water (two steps are needed)

Step 1: A magnet is used to separate the iron filings

Step 2: Evaporation is used to separate the salt and water

Mixture 4: gravel, sand, and sugar (four steps are needed)

Step 1: A strainer is used to separate the gravel

Step 2: Water is used to dissolve the sugar

Step 3: Filtration is used to separate the sand

Step 4: Evaporation is used to separate the sugar and water

Mixture 5: gravel, sand, sugar, and iron filings (five steps are needed)

Step 1: A strainer is used to separate the gravel

Step 2: A magnet is used to separate the iron filings

Step 3: Water is used to dissolve the sugar

Step 4: Filtration is used to separate the sand

Step 5: Evaporation is used to separate the sugar and water

What is a suspension?

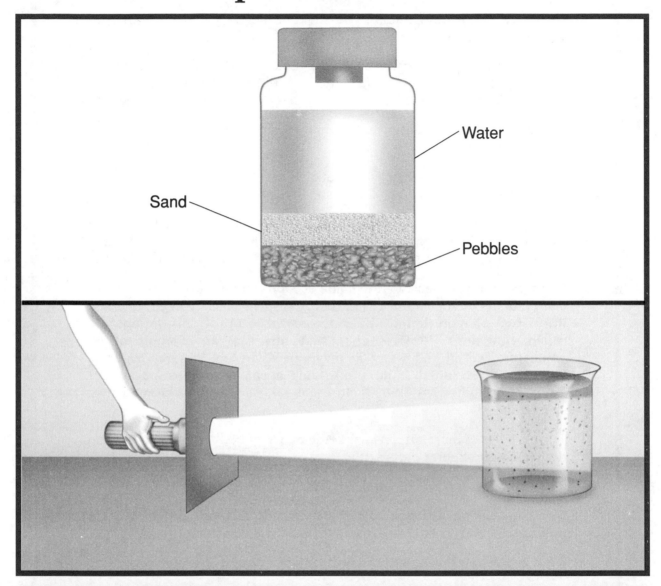

KEY TERMS

suspension: cloudy mixture of two or more substances that settle on standing

emulsion: suspension of two liquids

colloid: suspension in which the particles are permanently suspended

Tyndall effect: scattering of a light beam by particles in a colloid

LESSON 14 | What is a suspension?

Before you pour orange juice, you shake it. Before you spoon out vegetable soup, you stir it.

Orange juice and vegetable soup are mixtures. But they are not like solutions. The parts of solutions dissolve and do not settle. Mixtures like orange juice and vegetable soup do not dissolve. The parts do settle out.

Mixtures that do not dissolve and that do settle are called **suspensions** [suh-SPEN-shunz].

You have many suspensions in your home. Salad dressing and fruit juices are suspensions. So is liquid shoe polish.

Have you ever read the label on a salad dressing bottle? Some labels may say "Shake well before using." These bottles contain suspensions. In fact, any mixture that you see settling or that needs mixing is a suspension.

Many common suspensions are made of solids and liquids. A suspension can be made of solids and gases, too. A suspension may even be made up of two or more liquids. Suspensions made up of only liquids are called **emulsions** [i-MUL-shunz]. Mayonnaise is an example of an emulsion. The oil and water in mayonnaise are able to stay together because egg is added as an emulsifying agent. Emulsions are special kinds of **colloids** [KAHL-oyd]. In a colloid, particles are permanently suspended.

The particles of most suspensions settle by weight. The heavy parts settle first. Then the lighter parts settle.

The parts of a suspension are large. You can see them easily.

Most suspensions are cloudy. The suspended particles stop light. Light that hits the particles is reflected. This is why suspensions are cloudy.

Now you know several important properties of suspensions:

- The particles in suspensions do not dissolve.
- The particles in suspensions settle out. They separate into layers by weight.
- Suspensions are cloudy and uneven.
- The solid particles of a suspension are large. You can see them.
- Suspended solids reflect light.

WHICH SETTLES FIRST?

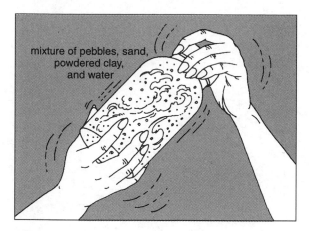

Figure A

Figure B

Place some pebbles, sand, and powdered clay into a jar.

Add water nearly to the top. Cover the jar tightly and shake.

Let it stand for five minutes. Observe what happens.

1. Which pieces settled first? _____pebbles_____

2. They are the _____largest_____ pieces.
   _{largest, smallest}

3. They also are the _____heaviest_____ pieces.
   _{lightest, heaviest}

4. Which settled last? __powdered clay__

5. They are the _____smallest_____ .
   _{largest, smallest}

6. They also are the _____lightest_____ .
   _{lightest, heaviest}

7. This shows that when a suspension settles, the _____heaviest_____ pieces settle
   _{heaviest, lightest}
   first and the _____lightest_____ pieces settle last.
   _{heaviest, lightest}

8. Usually, the heavy pieces are _____larger_____ ; the light pieces are
   _{smaller, larger}
   _____smaller_____ .
   _{smaller, larger}

CLAY AND WATER

Figure C

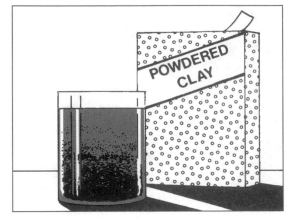

Figure D

Stir some powdered clay into a jar of water. Let it stand. Notice what happens.

1. Powdered clay in water _____is_____ a mixture.
   is, is not

2. The clay _____does not_____ dissolve.
   does, does not

3. The clay pieces _____do_____ settle.
   do, do not

4. Clay in water makes a mixture called a _____suspension_____ .
   liquid solution, suspension

5. The parts of a suspension _____do not_____ dissolve.
   do, do not

6. The parts of a suspension _____do_____ settle out.
   do, do not

MATCHING

Match each term in Column A with its description in Column B. Write the correct letter in the space provided.

	Column A	Column B
__a__	1. mixture	**a)** reflect light
__c__	2. suspension	**b)** settle last
__e__	3. heavy pieces	**c)** cloudy mixture of two or more substances that settle on standing
__b__	4. light pieces	**d)** liquid suspension
__d__	5. emulsion	**e)** settle first

92

WHAT IS THE TYNDALL EFFECT?

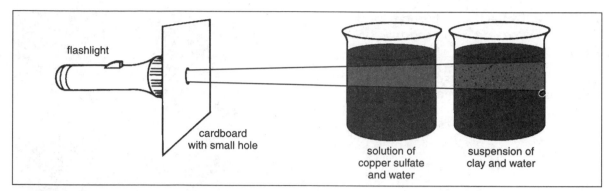

Figure E

What You Need (Materials)   2 beakers   powdered clay
                                  copper sulfate   flashlight
                                  water   cardboard with a hole

What to Do (Procedure)

1. Fill a beaker with a solution of copper sulfate and water.

2. Fill another beaker with a suspension of clay and water. Mix both mixtures well.

3. Place the beakers on the table next to one another.

4. Let the clay water settle for about two minutes.

5. Shine a flashlight through both beakers as in Figure E.

What You Saw and Learned (Observations)

1. You _____cannot_____ see particles in the solution.
        can, cannot

2. You _____can_____ see particles in the suspension.
        can, cannot

The reflection of light by suspended particles is called the **Tyndall effect**.

3. You can see suspended particles because they _____do_____ stop light.
                                                  do, do not

Something to Think About (Conclusions)

1. The Tyndall effect _____does_____ help us identify a suspension.
                       does, does not

2. The Tyndall effect also helps us identify the _____size_____ of suspended particles.
                                                  size, kind

3. Which kind of mixture shows the Tyndall effect? _____suspension_____
                                                    solution, suspension

4. Which kind of mixture does not show the Tyndall effect? _____solution_____
                                                            solution, suspension

WHO WAS THE TYNDALL EFFECT NAMED FOR?

The Tyndall effect was named for John Tyndall. He was a 19th century British scientist.

He studied many things. One was how light passes through the air in different places.

Figure F

Complete the chart below.

	Solutions	Suspensions
1. Do the parts dissolve?	yes	no
2. Do the particles settle?	no	yes
3. Is the mixture clear?	yes	no
4. Is the mixture cloudy?	no	yes
5. Do the particles reflect light?	no	yes
6. Can you see the particles?	no	yes

TRUE OR FALSE

In the space provided, write "true" if the sentence is true. Write "false" if the sentence is false.

True	1. Suspensions are mixtures.
True	2. The particles in suspensions settle out.
False	3. Suspensions are transparent.
True	4. Suspensions are cloudy.
True	5. Suspended pieces settle by weight.
False	6. In a suspension, heavy pieces settle last.
False	7. Suspension particles are the size of molecules.
True	8. The particles in suspensions stop light.

COLLOIDS

You have learned that the solid parts of a regular suspension settle out. A colloid is a special kind of suspension. The solid particles in a colloid <u>do not</u> settle out.

The particles in a colloid are larger than molecules. But they are much smaller than the particles in a regular suspension. The particles are so small and so light that they stay in suspension. They do not settle by themselves.

Most colloids look like solutions—transparent and evenly mixed. You cannot see the suspended particles easily. But with the beam of light, the tiny particles show up in the Tyndall test. Some colloid particles are so small that you need a microscope to see them.

Colloids cannot be separated with filter paper. Special porcelain [POR-suh-lan] filters are needed.

COLLOID OR SOLUTION?

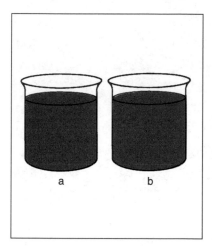

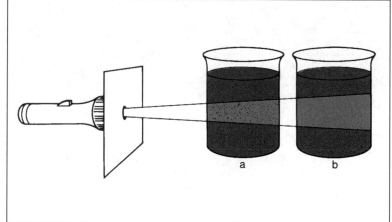

Figure G   **Figure H**

One of these mixtures is a solution. The other is a colloid.

They both look the same until we shine a beam of light through them.

1. Beaker _____a_____ shows the Tyndall effect.
   <small>a, b</small>

2. Beaker _____b_____ does not show the Tyndall effect.
   <small>a, b</small>

3. The solution is in beaker _____b_____ .
   <small>a, b</small>

4. The colloid is in beaker _____a_____ .
   <small>a, b</small>

5. ____Solution____ particles are the size of molecules.
   <small>Colloid, Solution</small>

6. ____Colloid____ particles are larger than molecules.
   <small>Colloid, Solution</small>

Figure I

Why do "quiet" lakes have clear water? Accept all logical responses. Likely responses include that in "quiet" lakes, water is not stirred up and moved around by air or water currents. The sediments settle to the bottom and stop there. Since there are no particles of sediment in the water, the water is clear.

How can the parts of a suspension be separated?

KEY TERMS

coagulation: use of chemicals to make the particles in a suspension clump together

filtration: separation of particles in a suspension by passing it through paper or other substances

LESSON 15 | How can the parts of a suspension be separated?

A cook drains off the cooking water from spaghetti. The wind makes dust fly in the air, but it settles. Spaghetti in water and dust in the air are both suspensions. In both examples, the parts of the suspension separated.

Many kinds of suspensions must be separated. Sometimes, nature separates the parts. Other times we must do it ourselves—or help nature along.

There are four ways to separate suspensions. They are **filtration** [fil-TRAY-shun], **sedimentation** [sed-uh-men-TAY-shun], **spinning**, and **coagulation** [koh-ag-yoo-LAY-shun].

FILTRATION Filtration is the same as straining. A filter has holes. Pieces smaller than the holes pass right through. Larger pieces are trapped by the filter.

Filters come in many sizes. Some have large holes. Some have small holes. The size of the filter you use depends upon the size of the particles you want to separate.

SEDIMENTATION Nature does this job itself. In sedimentation, the suspension just "sits." Gravity makes the pieces settle to the bottom of their containers.

SPINNING Spinning speeds settling. Spinning builds a strong outward force. The force pushes the pieces to the bottom of the container quickly.

COAGULATION Coagulation also speeds settling. Coagulation uses chemicals. The chemicals make small particles lump together. They become heavy and settle fast.

Coagulation occurs when you cut yourself. Chemicals in your blood cause the blood to coagulate and form a clot.

FILTRATION

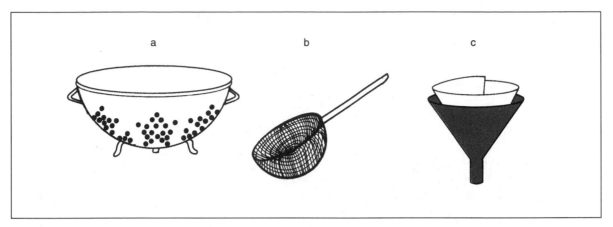

Figure A

1. Which filter separates out the largest pieces? _____a_____

2. Which one separates out the smallest pieces? _____c_____

3. Which filter would you use to strain spaghetti? _____a_____

4. Does filtration use chemicals? _____no_____

SEDIMENTATION

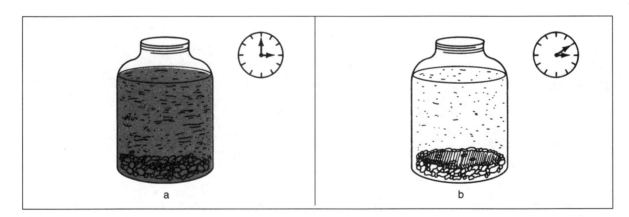

Figure B

1. In sedimentation:

   a) the heaviest pieces settle _____first_____ .

first, last

   b) the lightest particles settle _____last_____ .

first, last

2. Sedimentation is done by _____gravity_____ .

gravity, spinning

3. Does sedimentation use chemicals? _____no_____

Figure C

There are suspensions of clay and water in the can and the beaker.

1. The clay pieces will settle first in the _____can_____ .
   _{beaker, can}

2. The pieces in the beaker are settling by _____gravity_____ .
   _{spinning, gravity}

3. The pieces in the can are settling by _____spinning_____ .
   _{spinning, gravity}

4. Spinning causes an _____outward_____ force.
   _{outward, inward}

5. Spinning _____speeds_____ settling.
   _{speeds, slows}

6. Does spinning use chemicals? _____no_____

COAGULATION

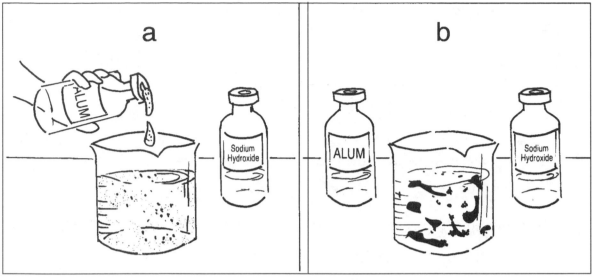

Figure D A B

1. The suspension in beaker B is settling by _____coagulation_____ .
   <u>coagulation, sedimentation</u>

2. Coagulation makes small particles _____lump together_____ .
   <u>lump together, move apart</u>

3. Coagulated particles become _____heavier_____ .
   <u>heavier, lighter</u>

4. Heavy particles settle more _____quickly_____ than light ones.
   <u>slowly, quickly</u>

5. Coagulation uses _____chemicals_____ and then gravity.
   <u>spinning, chemicals</u>

WHEN ARE SUSPENSIONS SEPARATED?

You have learned four ways of removing particles from suspensions. These can be very useful. Here is one example.

Most places get their drinking water from rivers, lakes, or reservoirs. The water has sediment suspended in it. It must be removed so the water can be fit to drink.

Several steps are used to remove the sediment. You will learn about these steps in Lesson 21.

Figure E

FILL IN THE BLANK

Complete each statement using a term or terms from the list below. Write your answers in the spaces provided. Some words may be used more than once.

spinning	first	coagulation
last	chemicals	lump together
gravity	sedimentation	filtration
outward	speed up	does not

1. The four ways of separating the parts of a suspension are ___filtration___,
   ___sedimentation___, ___spinning___, ___coagulation___.

2. The method that separates a suspension by trapping particles is ___filtration___.

3. In sedimentation, ___gravity___ makes the particles settle.

4. Heavy particles settle ___first___.

5. Lightweight particles settle ___last___.

6. Spinning and coagulation ___speed up___ settling.

7. Spinning builds an ___outward___ force.

8. Spinning ___does not___ use chemicals.

9. Coagulation uses ___chemicals___ and then gravity to make particles settle.

10. Coagulation makes small pieces ___lump together___.

MATCHING

Match each term in Column A with its description in Column B. Write the correct letter in the space provided.

	Column A		Column B
_d_	1. gravity	a)	causes strong outward force
_e_	2. filtration	b)	do not dissolve
_a_	3. spinning	c)	lumps particles together
_b_	4. suspension particles	d)	pulls things down
_c_	5. coagulation	e)	traps particles

TRUE OR FALSE

In the space provided, write "true" if the sentence is true. Write "false" if the sentence is false.

<u>True</u>   **1.** Suspended particles can be separated.

<u>False</u>   **2.** Filtration separates pieces by weight.

<u>False</u>   **3.** All filters are the same size.

<u>True</u>   **4.** Sedimentation uses gravity.

<u>False</u>   **5.** Spinning causes an inward force.

<u>True</u>   **6.** Spinning and coagulation speed sedimentation.

<u>False</u>   **7.** Filtration uses chemicals.

<u>False</u>   **8.** Spinning uses chemicals.

<u>False</u>   **9.** Sedimentation uses chemicals.

<u>True</u>   **10.** Coagulation uses chemicals.

WORD SCRAMBLE

Below are several scrambled words you have used in this Lesson. Unscramble the words and write your answers in the spaces provided.

1. NORFATILIT   FILTRATION

2. DOTRAWU   OUTWARD

3. NIPSNGIN   SPINNING

4. TAGYVIR   GRAVITY

5. GALUNOTIAOC   COAGULATION

6. TATMENNIODESI   SEDIMENTATION

7. CALCHEMSI   CHEMICALS

COMPLETE THE CHART

*Complete the chart by filling in the missing information. Identify whether each statement describes separation of a suspension by **filtration**, **coagulation**, or **spinning**, by placing an X in the correct column.*

	Description	Filtration	Coagulation	Spinning
1.	Particles stick together.		X	
2.	Particles are caught on paper.	X		
3.	Motion causes particles to be pulled out of a suspension.			X
4.	Chemicals are added to the suspension.		X	

REACHING OUT

After sediment from a suspension settles, how can you separate it from the liquid?

Student responses will vary. Likely responses may include: to pour off the liquid,

or to let the liquid evaporate.

What is a solution?

KEY TERMS

solution: mixture in which one substance is evenly mixed with another substance

solute: substance that is dissolved in a solvent

solvent: substance in which a solute dissolves

soluble: able to dissolve

dissolve: to cause to go into solution; to become liquid

LESSON 16 | What is a solution?

You can be a magician! Just add sugar to warm water and stir thoroughly. Abracadabra! The sugar disappears!

But is the sugar really gone? No. The sugar and water just mix together. They mix completely. The sugar just seems to disappear.

Sugar and water together form a mixture. There are several kinds of mixtures. Sugar and water form a special kind of mixture. They form a **solution**. There are many kinds of solutions.

A solution has two parts: a **solute** [SAHL-yoot] and a **solvent**. The solvent is usually a liquid. The solute is what "disappears" in the solvent. The solute may be a solid, a gas, or another liquid.

A solution is formed when the solute **dissolves**. The solute spreads out evenly throughout the solvent. The substance that dissolves is said to be **soluble** [SAHL-yoo-bul].

In the example of sugar and water, the water is the solvent. Water dissolves sugar. The sugar is the solute. We say that sugar is soluble in water.

There are many kinds of solvents. There are many kinds of solutes. There are many kinds of solutions.

Remember, a mixture is a solution only if the solute dissolves and spreads out evenly.

SOLUTIONS AND THE STATES OF MATTER

All the examples in Figures A, B, and C are solutions.

Remember, there are three states of matter—solid, liquid, and gas.

Figure A

1. Name the states of matter in this solution (Figure A).

   ___solid___ and ___liquid___

2. The solute is the

   ___solid___ .
   solid, liquid

3. The solvent is the

   ___liquid___ .
   solid, liquid

Figure B

4. Name the states of matter of this solution (Figure B).

   ___liquid___ and

   ___gas___ .

5. The solute is the

   ___gas___ .
   gas, liquid

6. The solvent is the

   ___liquid___ .
   gas, liquid

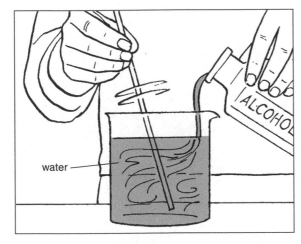

Figure C

7. Name the states of matter of this solution (Figure C).

   ___liquid___ and ___liquid___ .

NOTE: In solutions where all the parts are liquid, we usually say the liquid present in the greater amount is the solvent and the other liquid is the solute.

COMPLETING SENTENCES

Choose the correct word or term for each statement. Write your choice in the spaces provided.

1. A liquid solution has at least one ____liquid____ .

solid, liquid, gas

2. The solute in a solution ____can be any state of matter____ .

must be a gas, must be a solid, can be any state of matter

3. In solutions of liquids and solids or of liquids and gases, the solvent is always the

    ____liquid____ .

solid, liquid, gas

4. In solutions of all liquids, we usually name the liquid present in the ____greater____

greater, lesser

amount the solvent.

WHICH ARE SOLUTIONS?

Ten mixtures you know are listed below. Some are solutions, some are not. Think about each mixture, then fill in the boxes.

	Mixture	Do the substances dissolve? (Write (YES or NO.)	If the substances dissolved, name the solute (or solutes).	name the solvent.
1.	sugar water	yes	sugar	water
2.	muddy water	no	—	—
3.	salty water	yes	salt	water
4.	pebbles in water	no	—	—
5.	instant coffee drink	yes	instant coffee crystals	water
6.	orange juice	no	—	—
7.	oil and water	no	—	—
8.	instant tea drink	yes	instant tea mix	water
9.	ocean water	yes	salts	water

FILL IN THE BLANK

Complete each statement using a term or terms from the list below. Write your answers in the spaces provided. Some words may be used more than once.

mixture	solution	sugar water
two	liquid	solvent
solid	gas	solute
soluble	water	

1. Different things close together make up a _____mixture_____ .

2. A _____solution_____ is a special kind of mixture.

3. An example of a solution is _____sugar water_____ .

4. A solution has _____two_____ main parts.

5. One part of a solution is usually a _____liquid_____ .

6. The liquid part of a solution is called the _____solvent_____ .

7. The other part of a solution can be a _____solid_____ , or a _____liquid_____ ,

    or a _____gas_____ .

8. The part of a solution that mixes into the solvent is called the _____solute_____ .

9. A solute that dissolves in a solvent is said to be _____soluble_____ .

10. Sugar is soluble in _____water_____ .

MATCHING

Match each term in Column A with its description in Column B. Write the correct letter in the space provided.

	Column A		Column B
__c__	1. mixture	a)	means "able to dissolve"
__e__	2. solute	b)	liquid part of a solution
__b__	3. solvent	c)	different things close together
__d__	4. solution	d)	a special kind of mixture
__a__	5. soluble	e)	part of a solution that is dissolved

Be a detective! How can you tell if a mixture is a solution? We will learn more in the following Lessons. Meanwhile, see if you can figure out the clues.

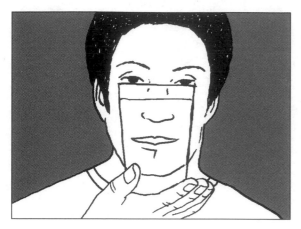

Figure D

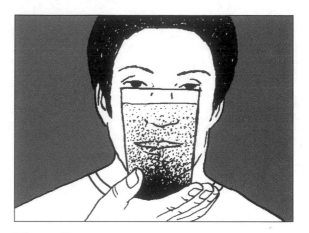

Figure E

- This is a mixture of sugar and water.

- Sugar and water is a solution.

- This is a mixture of muddy water.

- Muddy water is not a solution.

Answer YES or NO to these questions.

		Muddy Water	**Sugar Water**
1.	Are the parts evenly mixed?	no	yes
2.	Can you see the separate parts?	yes	no
3.	Do particles fall to the bottom?	yes	no
4.	Can you see clearly through this mixture?	no	yes

How can you tell if a mixture is a solution?

In your own words, list the clues.

   Student responses will vary. Likely responses include: In a solution, the

   solute and solvent are evenly mixed; you cannot see the different parts of a

   solution. The solute does not settle out in a solution, it stays evenly mixed.

   A solution is clear so you can see through it.

What are the properties of solutions?

KEY TERMS

properties: characteristics used to describe a substance

homogeneous: uniform; the same all the way through

transparent: material that transmits light easily

LESSON 17 | What are the properties of solutions?

What happens when you add salt to a jar of water and stir? The salt disappears. You have made a solution. Does the same thing happen when you add sand to water? No. The sand settles to the bottom of the jar.

How can we tell if a mixture is a solution or not? We can tell by its **properties** [PROP-ur-tees]. Properties tell us how a kind of matter looks and acts.

These are the properties of solutions:

(1) The parts dissolve and become the size of molecules.
(2) Solutions are **homogeneous** [hoh-muh-JEE-nee-us].
(3) Solutions are **transparent** [trans-PER-unt].
(4) Solutions do not settle out.

MOLECULE SIZE You know that matter is made up of tiny atoms. Most matter is made up of <u>groups</u> of atoms called molecules. In a solution, the particles of solute dissolve. They break up until they are the size of molecules.

HOMOGENEOUS Homogeneous means evenly mixed—the same all through. Because the particles are the size of molecules they weigh very little. They move around and spread out evenly.

TRANSPARENT You can see clearly through something that is transparent. Glass is transparent. So are solutions. The molecules that make them up are tiny. They do not block out light. Light passes right through.

THE PARTS NEVER SETTLE OUT Something that settles out drops to the bottom of its container. The parts of a solution never separate. They never settle out no matter how long they sit. That is because the molecules are light. They keep bouncing around. This also keeps the solution homogeneous.

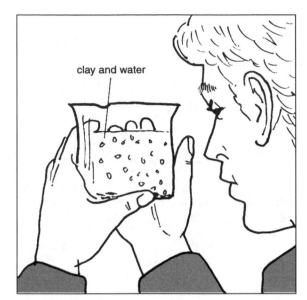

Figure A   **Figure B**

Look at Figure A.

1. Can you see the sugar particles? _____no_____
   _{yes, no}

2. The sugar _____did_____ dissolve.
   _{did, did not}

3. The sugar is now _____the size of molecules_____ .
   _{the size of molecules, much larger than the size of molecules}

4. Can the boy see through the sugar water? _____yes_____
   _{yes, no}

5. The sugar water is _____transparent_____ .
   _{cloudy, transparent}

6. The mixture _____is_____ evenly mixed.
   _{is, is not}

7. It _____is_____ homogeneous.
   _{is, is not}

8. The sugar _____is not_____ settling.
   _{is, is not}

9. Sugar water _____is_____ a solution.
   _{is, is not}

Look at Figure B.

1. Can you see the clay particles? _____yes_____
   _{yes, no}

2. The clay _____did not_____ dissolve.
   _{did, did not}

3. The clay particles are _____much larger than the size of molecules_____ .
   _{the size of molecules, much larger than the size of molecules}

4. Can the boy see clearly through the mixture? _____no_____
yes, no

5. The clay water is _____cloudy_____ .
cloudy, transparent

6. The mixture _____is not_____ evenly mixed.
is, is not

7. It _____is not_____ homogeneous.
is, is not

8. The clay _____is_____ settling out.
is, is not

9. Clay water _____is not_____ a solution.
is, is not

FILL IN THE BLANK

Complete each statement using a term or terms from the list below. Write your answers in the spaces provided. Some words may be used more than once.

solutions	moving around	light
drop	is not	clay water
molecules	transparent	small in size

1. When we can see clearly through something we say it is _____transparent_____ .

2. _____Solutions_____ are transparent.

3. _____Clay water_____ is not transparent.

4. Clay water _____is not_____ a solution.

5. The parts of a solution are the size of _____molecules_____ .

6. The molecules of a solution do not block _____light_____ .

7. To "settle out" means to _____drop_____ .

8. The parts of _____solutions_____ do not settle out.

9. Solutions do not settle out because the parts are too _____small in size_____ .

10. The molecules in liquid solutions are always _____moving around_____ .

WHICH IS HOMOGENEOUS?

The dots stand for copper sulfate molecules. The liquid is water.

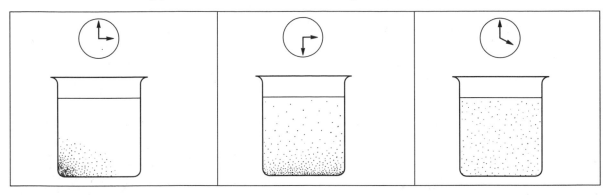

Figure C   **Figure D**   **Figure E**

1. Which figure shows a homogeneous mixture? ____Figure E____

2. **a)** The mixtures in Figures ___C___ and ___D___ are not solutions.

    b) They are not liquid solutions because they _____are not_____ homogeneous.
            <small>are, are not</small>

3. **a)** The mixtures that are not solutions _____could_____ become solutions.
            <small>could, could not</small>

    b) They would be solutions if all the _____solute_____ dissolved, and spread out
            evenly.   <small>solute, solvent</small>

4. Think about this: What would you do to make the mixtures that are not homogeneous,
    become homogeneous fast?

    Student responses will vary. Likely responses include: mix the mixtures, stir

    the mixtures, or shake the mixtures.

MATCHING

*Match each term in Column A with its description in Column B. Write the correct letter in the
space provided.*

	Column A	**Column B**
___c___	**1.** molecule	**a)** evenly mixed
___a___	**2.** homogeneous	**b)** drop
___b___	**3.** settle out	**c)** tiny part of matter
___e___	**4.** properties	**d)** clear
___d___	**5.** transparent	**e)** things that help us identify matter

TRUE OR FALSE

In the space provided, write "true" if the sentence is true. Write "false" if the sentence is false.

____True____   **1.** Anything we can see through clearly is transparent.

____False____   **2.** Every mixture is homogeneous.

____False____   **3.** Sand becomes the size of molecules when it is in water.

____True____   **4.** Solutions are transparent.

____False____   **5.** Muddy water is transparent.

____True____   **6.** Muddy water settles out.

____True____   **7.** The parts of liquids are the size of molecules.

____True____   **8.** Salt water is a solution.

____False____   **9.** Solutions settle out.

____True____   **10.** The molecules of solutions are always moving around.

REACHING OUT

Transparent, translucent, and opaque are three words that have to do with light. Give a definition of each word in the spaces below. (You may use a dictionary.) Next to each definition give an example of each.

Transparent _____

____material that transmits light easily____

_____

Translucent _____

____material that transmits some light____

_____

Opaque _____

____material that blocks light____

_____

Figure F

Lesson 18

How can the strength of a solution be changed?

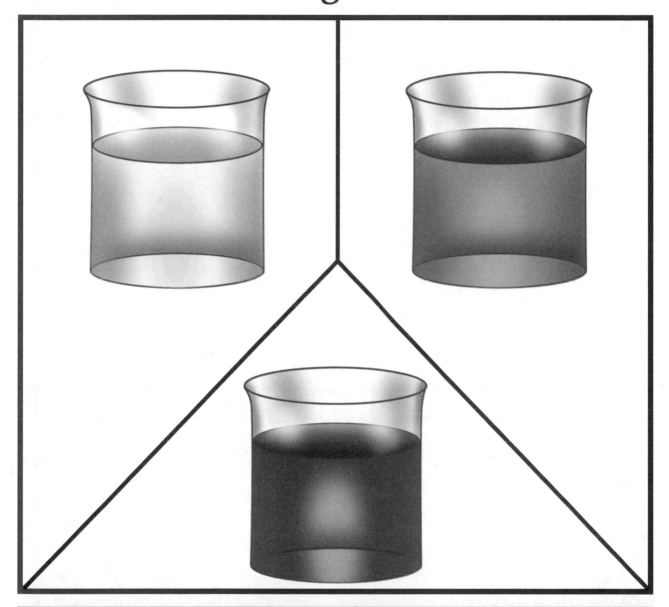

KEY TERMS

dilute solution: weak solution

concentrated solution: strong solution

saturated solution: solution containing all the solute it can hold at a given temperature

LESSON 18 | How can the strength of a solution be changed?

Some people like strong coffee. Others like it weak. What makes coffee strong or weak? You know that if you add more coffee it becomes stronger. If you add more water, it becomes weaker. A cup of coffee is like any solution. It comes in many strengths.

We use these terms to describe how strong a solution is:

- **dilute** [di-LEWT] **solution**

- **concentrated** [KAHN-sun-trayt-ed] **solution**

- **saturated** [SACH-uh-rayt-id] **solution**

DILUTE A dilute solution is a weak solution. It has very little solute dissolved in the solvent.

CONCENTRATED A concentrated solution is a strong solution. It has more solute dissolved in it than a dilute solution has.

SATURATED A saturated solution is an extra-strong solution. It has so much solute that no more can dissolve. If we tried to add more solute, it would just drop to the bottom. More solute would dissolve only if the mixture were heated.

We can change the strength of a solution. We do this by changing the amount of solute or solvent.

Terms like "dilute" and "concentrated" help us compare solutions.

HOW STRONG IS THE SOLUTION?

A cup of instant tea is a liquid solution.

Two different cups of tea are shown in Figures A and B. Study them. Then fill in the blanks.

Figure A   **Figure B**

1. The instant tea _____does_____ dissolve.

does, does not

2. A cup of tea _____is_____ a solution.

is, is not

3. In both solutions the solute is the _____tea_____ .

tea, water

4. In both solutions the solvent is the _____water_____ .

tea, water

5. The cup of tea in Figure A has a _____lot_____ of solute compared to the solution in Figure B.

lot, little bit

6. The solution in Figure A is _____stronger_____ than the solution in Figure B.

stronger, weaker

7. The solution in Figure A is more _____concentrated_____ than the solution in Figure B.

concentrated, dilute

8. The solution in Figure B _____has_____ the same kind of solute and solvent as Figure A.

has, does not have

9. The amount of solvent is ____the same____ in both solutions.

the same, different

10. The amount of solute is ____different____ in both solutions.

the same, different

11. There is ____less____ solute in Figure B.

more, less

12. This solution is ____weaker____ than the solution in Figure A.

stronger, weaker

13. This solution is ____more dilute____ than the solution in Figure A.

more concentrated, more dilute

COLOR AND STRENGTH OF SOLUTIONS

Sometimes, color tells us about the strength of a solution. The darker the color, the stronger the solution. The lighter the color, the weaker the solution. We can use color only when we compare similar solutions.

Of Figures A and B on Page 119,

1. Which figure shows a darker solution? ____Figure A____

2. Which figure shows a lighter solution? ____Figure B____

3. Which solution is stronger? ____Figure A____

4. Which solution is weaker? ____Figure B____

5. Why can color help us compare the strengths of these mixtures? _____

   When more solute is dissolved in a solution, the color gets darker. More solute

   dissolved in a given amount of solvent makes a stronger solution.

COMPARING CONCENTRATIONS

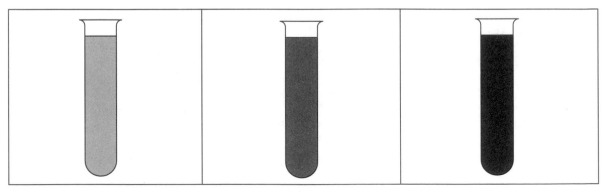

Figure C   **Figure D**   **Figure E**

Look at Figures C, D, and E. Each test tube contains a solution. The kind of solute and solvent is the same in each.

1. Which is the strongest? _____Figure E_____

2. Which is the weakest? _____Figure C_____

3. Which has the most solute? _____Figure E_____

4. Which has the least solute? _____Figure C_____

5. Which one is closest to being saturated? _____Figure E_____

A SATURATED SOLUTION

Figure F   **Figure G**

The beakers in Figures F and G contain solutions. The kind of solute and solvent is the same in each. Some additional solute has been added to each. Both mixtures have been stirred well.

1. Which is not saturated? _____Figure G_____

2. Which one is saturated? _____Figure F_____

3. How do you know? ___There are particles in the bottom of the beaker._____

_____

4. Take a guess! How can we make the extra solute dissolve?_____

___Student responses will vary. Likely responses include: if the solution is stirred___

___or heated; or if more solvent is added._____

FILL IN THE BLANK

Complete each statement using a term or terms from the list below. Write your answers in the spaces provided.

> lighter   strengths   saturated
> very little   raising the temperature   a lot
> color   concentrated   darker
> dilute

1. Solutions come in different ____strengths____ .

2. A weak solution is called ____dilute____ .

3. A strong solution is called ____concentrated____ .

4. Dilute solutions have ____very little____ solute.

5. Concentrated solutions have ____a lot____ of solute.

6. A solution that can dissolve no more solute is called ____saturated____ .

7. We can make a saturated solution dissolve more solute by

   ____raising the temperature____ .

8. Sometimes we can use ____color____ to compare the strengths of solutions.

9. In comparing strength by color, the ____darker____ the color, the stronger the solution.

10. In comparing strength by color, the ____lighter____ the color, the weaker the solution.

MATCHING

Match each term in Column A with its description in Column B. Write the correct letter in the space provided.

	Column A	**Column B**
__e__	1. dilute solution	a) extra solute does not dissolve
__c__	2. concentrated solution	b) more solute dissolves
__a__	3. saturated solution	c) strong solution
__b__	4. raising the temperature	d) sometimes used to compare solution strengths
__d__	5. color	e) weak solution

WORD SEARCH

The list on the left contains words that you have used in this Lesson. Find and circle each word where it appears in the box. The spellings may go in any direction: up, down, left, right, or diagonally.

MOLECULE

SOLUTE

SOLVENT

DILUTE

SOLUBLE

GAS

DISSOLVE

SOLID

MIXTURE

LIQUID

SATURATE

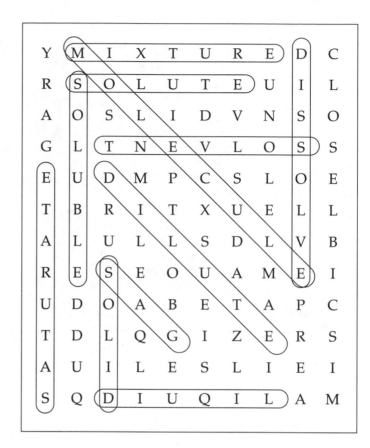

REACHING OUT

Why can color be used only for comparing similar solutions and not for comparing different solutions?

Student responses will vary. Likely responses include: color and strength of solute

may be different. Accept all logical responses.

SCIENCE *EXTRA*

Crystals

What happens when wood burns? What happens to the metal of an old car? Chemical changes produce ashes from the wood and rust from the metal of the car. Chemical changes never stop occurring. They happen inside our bodies, in deep caves, and even on city streets.

Chemical changes also form some types of crystals. Other crystals, like ice crystals, are a result of physical changes. All crystals form definite shapes and sizes. If you look at sugar or salt crystals with a hand lens, you can see their shapes. Snowflakes are tiny ice crystals that come together in a different way over and over again. That is why every snowflake is unique. Stalactites and stalagmites found in deep caves are crystals. They formed over millions of years. Rock candy is a lump of sugar crystals that you can eat. You can make your own crystal garden and watch the crystals grow over several days. Here's how:

- Mix 4 tablespoons of blueing, 4 tablespoons of salt, and 1 tablespoon of household ammonia.
- Pour the mixture over a brick that is set on a ceramic plate or bowl.

- If desired, add several drops of different food colors on the brick.
- Set the brick in an undisturbed area and observe.
- If possible, photograph the crystals daily to record their growth over time.

The brick will soon be covered with crystals. If left alone, the crystals will keep growing. Why does this happen? A chemical reaction takes place between the blueing, salt, ammonia, and oxygen in the air. The reaction makes crystals grow on the brick.

For comparison, repeat the experiment using a different solution. This time, mix 1 tablespoon of Epsom salts dissolved in 1/4 cup of warm water. This mixture and the previous mixture both produce a chemical change. Both mixtures produce crystals. However, the ingredients in each mixture are different. Therefore, the crystals that grow are different.

If you have time, find out about other types of crystals. How do those crystals compare with the ones you made?

How can solutes be made to dissolve faster?

LESSON 19 | How can solutes be made to dissolve faster?

What do you do after you add sugar to a drink? You stir. But why? You stir because you know that mixing makes sugar dissolve faster.

Stirring makes any solute dissolve faster.

Now here is another question. Which will dissolve faster, a lump of sugar or small grains of sugar? You know from experience that the smaller the pieces the faster they will dissolve.

Now let us tackle another question. Which will dissolve sugar faster, cold water or hot water?

From your experience you know that solutes dissolve faster in hot water.

There are three ways to make solids dissolve faster:

- <u>Stir the mixture.</u>

- <u>Break the solute into smaller pieces.</u>

- <u>Heat the mixture.</u>

Doing any of these things makes a solute dissolve faster. Doing two or all three dissolves the solute much faster.

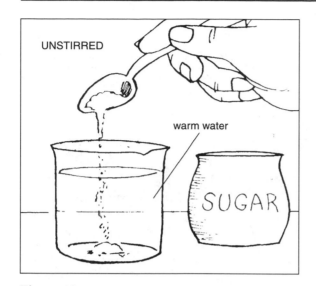

Figure A

Pour some granulated sugar into a glass of warm water. Do not stir.

Figure B

Pour the same amount of granulated sugar into another glass of warm water. Then stir.

Notice how fast the sugar dissolves in each glass.

1. Stirring makes a solute dissolve _____faster_____ .

    faster, slower

Figure C

Pour some granulated sugar into cold water. Do not stir.

Figure D

Pour the same amount of granulated sugar into hot water. Do not stir.

Notice how fast the sugar dissolves in each beaker.

2. A solute dissolves faster in a _____hot_____ solvent.
   hot, cold

3. A solute dissolves slower in a _____cold_____ solvent.
   hot, cold

4. Heat makes a solute dissolve _____faster_____ .
   slower, faster

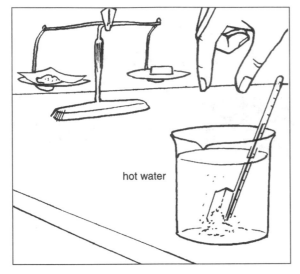

Figure E

Put a lump of sugar into a glass of hot water. Do not stir.

Figure F

Pour one teaspoon of granulated sugar into a glass of hot water. Do not stir.

Notice how fast the sugar dissolves.

5. Big pieces dissolve _____slower_____ than small pieces.
   slower, faster

6. Small pieces dissolve _____faster_____ than large pieces.
   slower, faster

7. Crushing makes solutes dissolve _____faster_____ .
   slower, faster

NOW TRY THESE

1. The two main parts of any liquid solution are the _____solute_____ and the _____solvent_____ .

2. The liquid part of a solution is called the _____solvent_____ .

3. The part of a solution that dissolves into the liquid is called the

_____solute_____ .

4. Three ways we can make a solid solute dissolve faster are:

_____stir the mixture_____ , _____break the solute into smaller pieces_____ ,

and _____heat the mixture_____ .

COMPLETE THE CHART

Complete the chart by filling in the missing information.

	If you . . .	then the solute dissolves faster.	slower.
1.	make the pieces larger,		✔
2.	make the pieces smaller,	✔	
3.	stir,	✔	
4.	do not stir,		✔
5.	heat the solvent,	✔	
6.	do not heat the solvent.		✔

TRUE OR FALSE

In the space provided, write "true" if the sentence is true. Write "false" if the sentence is false.

__True__ **1.** Stirring moves things around.

__False__ **2.** Crushing makes things larger.

__False__ **3.** Heat lowers temperature.

__True__ **4.** Stirring makes solutes dissolve faster.

__False__ **5.** Small pieces of solute dissolve slower than big pieces.

__True__ **6.** Heat makes solutes dissolve faster.

WORD SCRAMBLE

Below are several scrambled words you have used in this Lesson. Unscramble the words and write your answers in the spaces provided.

1. NEAHIGT   HEATING

2. TARSEF   FASTER

3. RIST   STIR

4. SCURH   CRUSH

5. SLEDSIVO   DISSOLVE

REACHING OUT

You put a piece of glass in water. It does not dissolve. You then crush it into tiny pieces.

Will the pieces dissolve? _____ no _____ Explain. _____

Student answers will vary. Likely responses include: no matter how small you crush

the glass, it will never dissolve because glass does not dissolve in water.

How can solutes change the freezing and boiling point of water?

LESSON 20 | How can solutes change the freezing and boiling point of water?

Most automobile engines are cooled with water. In the winter, it is very cold in most parts of the country. If the water freezes, it can ruin the engine.

Car owners add antifreeze to the car's cooling system. This prevents the water from changing to ice. The same antifreeze also protects the engine from boiling over in the hot summer.

How does antifreeze work? Antifreeze is a solution. It has solutes dissolved in a liquid. Antifreeze acts like a solute in a solution. Putting antifreeze in the water of the cooling system raises the boiling point of the water. It also lowers the freezing point of the water.

Certain (not all) dissolved solutes change the boiling point and freezing point of water. These dissolved solutes make it harder for water to freeze and boil.

This means that the water needs more cold to freeze and more heat to boil. The water freezes at a temperature lower than 0° C (32° F). It boils at a temperature higher than 100° C (212° F).

Adding more solutes lowers the freezing temperature and raises the boiling temperature even more. BUT THERE IS A LIMIT. After a certain amount of solute has been added, no more changes take place.

SOLUTES CHANGE BOILING AND FREEZING POINTS

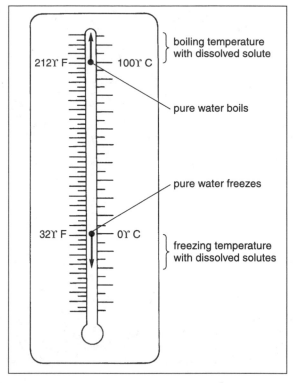

Certain solutes

<u>raise</u> the boiling temperature,
        and
<u>lower</u> the freezing temperature of water.

Figure A

HOW DOES SALT CHANGE THE BOILING OF WATER?

What You Need (Materials)

2 beakers   water
2 ring stands and clamps   salt
2 thermometers   2 Bunsen burners

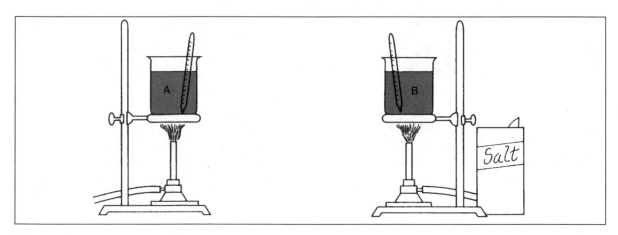

Figure B

How to Do the Experiment (Procedure)

1. Fill both beakers half full with water. Label one beaker A and the other B.

2. Stir a teaspoon of salt into beaker B only.

3. Set the beakers on the ring stands and place the thermometers in the water. Light the burners.

4. Observe the temperature at which the water boils in each beaker.

5. Put your observations on the chart below.

Boiling Point

PLAIN TAP WATER	100° C
SALT WATER	a few degrees higher than 100° C

What You Learned (Observations)

1. The tap water boiled at _____100_____ ° C.

2. The salt water boiled at _____100+_____ ° C.

3. The salt water boiled at a _____higher_____ temperature than the tap water.

higher, lower

4. Water boils at a _____higher_____ temperature when a solute is added.

higher, lower

Something To Think About (Conclusions)

1. Is salt water a solution? _____yes_____

2. Which part is the solute? _____salt_____

3. Which part is the solvent? _____water_____

4. How did salt change the boiling point of water? _____It raised the boiling point._____

134

Get two small plastic containers of the same size. Fill them half full with tap water.

Figure C

Dissolve a teaspoon of salt into one of the containers.

Label this container S.

Figure D

Place the containers in your freezer.

Check them every half hour.

Which one freezes first?

The unlabeled container; with no

salt added.

Figure E

1. The plain tap water froze _____faster_____ than the salt water.
   faster. slower

2. The salt water froze _____slower_____ than the plain tap water.
   faster. slower

3. Dissolved salt makes water _____more difficult_____ to freeze.
   easier, more difficult

TRUE OR FALSE

In the space provided, write "true" if the sentence is true. Write "false" if the sentence is false.

True   **1.** Adding certain solutes to water makes the water more difficult to freeze.

True   **2.** Adding certain solutes to water lowers the freezing point.

False   **3.** Adding certain solutes to water raises the freezing point.

False   **4.** Adding certain solutes to water makes it easier to boil.

True   **5.** Adding certain solutes to water raises the boiling point.

False   **6.** Adding certain solutes to water lowers the boiling point.

True   **7.** Antifreeze also acts as "anti-boil."

True   **8.** The freezing point of plain water is higher than the freezing point of salt water.

False   **9.** The boiling point of salt water is 100° C.

True   **10.** The freezing point of plain water is 0° C.

REACHING OUT

Why do you think people put rock salt on icy sidewalks?

Student responses will vary. Likely

responses include: the salt lowers

the freezing point of water,

therefore as the ice melts, the salt

mixes with the water. Salt water

will not freeze as rapidly.

Figure F

136

How can the parts of a solution be separated?

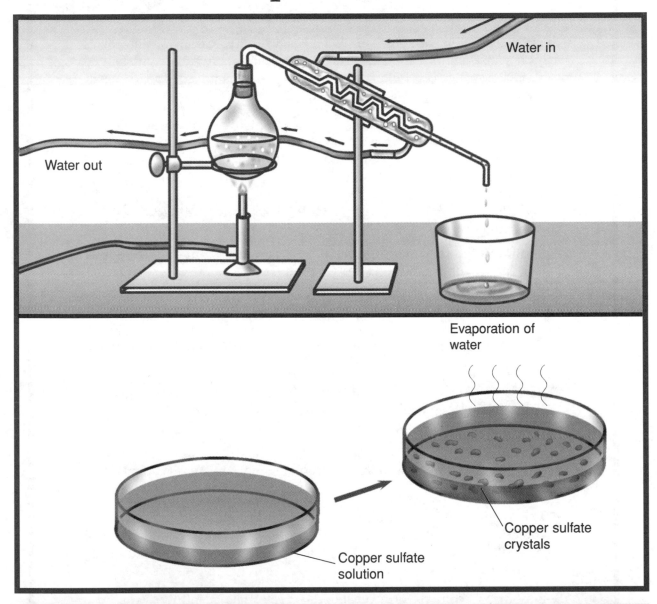

Water in

Water out

Evaporation of water

Copper sulfate crystals

Copper sulfate solution

KEY TERMS

evaporation: change of a liquid to a gas at the surface of the liquid

distillation: process of evaporating a liquid and then condensing the gas back into a liquid

condensation: change of a gas to a liquid

LESSON 21 | How can the parts of a solution be separated?

Everybody knows that ocean water tastes salty. Ocean water tastes salty because sodium chloride (NaCl)—common table salt—is dissolved in it. Ocean water is a liquid solution. The water is the solvent. The salt is one of many solutes dissolved in it.

How can you prove that ocean water contains dissolved salt? Simple! Place some ocean water into a shallow dish—and let it stand for a few days. Slowly the water disappears. The water changes to a gas, and escapes into the air. The salt stays behind as a solid.

The change of a liquid to a gas is called **evaporation** [i-vap-uh-RAY-shun]. You learned about this in Lesson 13.

Any liquid solution can be separated by evaporation. But only the solute is recovered. The solvent escapes into the air.

How can you recover both the solvent and the solute?

Filtration can't help. All the parts of a liquid solution are the size of molecules. They are so tiny, they pass right through the holes of even the filter paper.

There is another method called **distillation** [dis-tuh-LAY-shun]. Distillation recovers both the solute and the solvent of a liquid solution.

Distillation requires two steps:

• The first step is evaporation. The liquid changes to a gas (vapor). Heat speeds the process.

• The second step is **condensation** [kah-dun-SAY-shun]. The gas is cooled. As a result, it changes back to a liquid . . . and is collected. The solvent is pure. It has no solute in it. The solute remains behind in its solid form.

Some "dried" solutes form crystals. A crystal has a definite geometric shape. The crystal shape of a given solute is always the same.

EVAPORATION

See what happens when salt water evaporates. Figure A shows you the experiment.

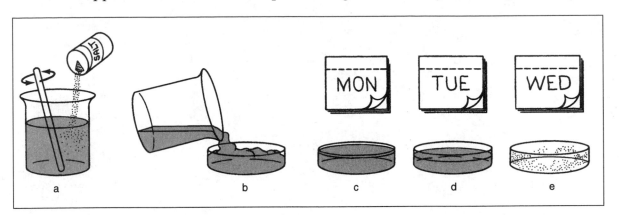

Figure A

1. Did the salt and water form a solution? _____yes_____

2. In salt water,   **a)** the solute is the _____salt_____ .
                                      salt, water

   b) the solvent is the _____water_____ .
                                      salt, water

3. Did the water from your dish evaporate? _____yes_____

4. Was anything left behind? _____yes_____

5. The _____solute_____ was left behind in its _____solid_____ form.
          solute, solvent   solid, liquid

6. Name the solid that was left behind. _____salt_____

7. Name the liquid that went into the air. _____water_____

8. When salt water is left in an open dish, the _____water_____ evaporates.
                                                  salt, water

9. In evaporation, a _____liquid_____ changes to a _____gas_____ .
                        gas, liquid   gas, liquid

10. When a solution evaporates, we get back _____only the solute_____

   _____ .
   only the solute, only the solvent, both the solute and solvent

139

CAN FILTERING SEPARATE A SOLUTE FROM A SOLVENT?

What You Need (Materials)

2 beakers
copper sulfate solution
funnel
filter paper
ring stand

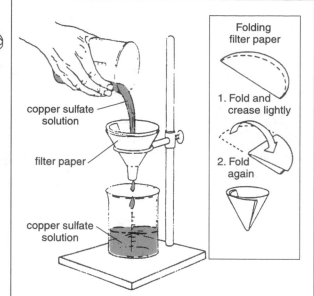

**How to Do the Experiment
(Procedure)**

1. Set up the ring stand with the
   funnel in place.

2. Fold the filter paper as shown in
   Figure B and place in the funnel.

3. Put the beaker under the funnel.

Figure B

4. Pour the copper sulfate solution through the filter paper.

What You Learned (Observations)

1. The solute _____was not_____ left behind in the filter paper.
   was, was not

2. The solvent _____was not_____ left behind in the filter paper.
   was, was not

3. The solute particles are _____smaller_____ than the holes in the filter paper.
   larger, smaller

4. The solvent particles are _____smaller_____ than the holes in the filter paper.
   larger, smaller

Something to Think About (Conclusions)

1. A solution _____cannot_____ be separated by filtering.
   can, cannot

2. The parts of a solution are _____the size of molecules_____ .
   the size of molecules, larger than the size of molecules

3. Filter paper holes are _____larger than the size of molecules_____ .
   the size of molecules, larger than the size of molecules

A DISTILLATION UNIT

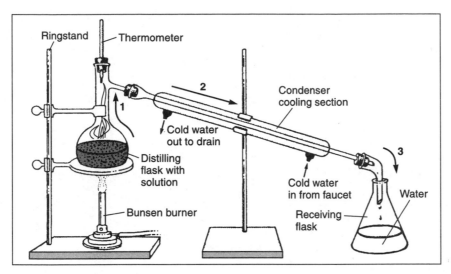

Figure C

How a Distillation Unit Works:

1. A solution is heated in a flask and the water turns to steam. Solids or liquids that have not reached their evaporation point remain in the flask.

2. The steam enters the condenser and is cooled. As it cools, it changes back to a liquid.

3. The condensed liquid comes out of the condenser and enters the receiving flask.

WHAT HAPPENS IN DISTILLATION?

Fill in the blank spaces. Check with Figure C as you read.

1. The solution is boiled in the boiler. The solvent evaporates. The solvent changes

    from a _____liquid_____ to a gas (water vapor).

2. The vapor moves out of the boiler. It goes into the inner tube of the cooling section.

3. The cold water in the outer tube cools the vapor. This makes the vapor condense.

    The vapor changes from a _____gas_____ back to a liquid.

4. The liquid drips into a container. It is pure. It has been distilled. It has no solute dissolved in it.

5. What happens to the solute? The solid solute stays behind in the boiler. It is now dried up. It is in solid form.

FILL IN THE BLANK

Complete each statement using a term or terms from the list below. Write your answers in the spaces provided. Some words may be used more than once.

filtering	distillation	drop
gas	larger	solvent
solute	heated	liquid
distilled		

1. When a solution evaporates, only the _____solvent_____ changes to a gas.

2. Evaporation happens faster when a solution is _____heated_____ .

3. Filter paper holes are _____larger_____ than the size of molecules.

4. Solutions cannot be separated by _____filtering_____ .

5. Evaporation saves only the _____solute_____ of a solution.

6. _____Distillation_____ gets back both the solute and the solvent from a solution.

7. In evaporation a _____liquid_____ changes to a _____gas_____ .

8. In condensation a _____gas_____ changes to a _____liquid_____ .

9. Condensation takes place when there is a _____drop_____ in temperature.

10. _____Distilled_____ water has no solutes in it.

WORD SCRAMBLE

Below are several scrambled words you have used in this Lesson. Unscramble the words and write your answers in the spaces provided.

1. NEDTASCONION _____CONDENSATION_____

2. TILLSIDNATIO _____DISTILLATION_____

3. NIOTRAPAEOV _____EVAPORATION_____

4. LOTSUE _____SOLUTE_____

5. THEA _____HEAT_____

Acids and Bases

Lesson
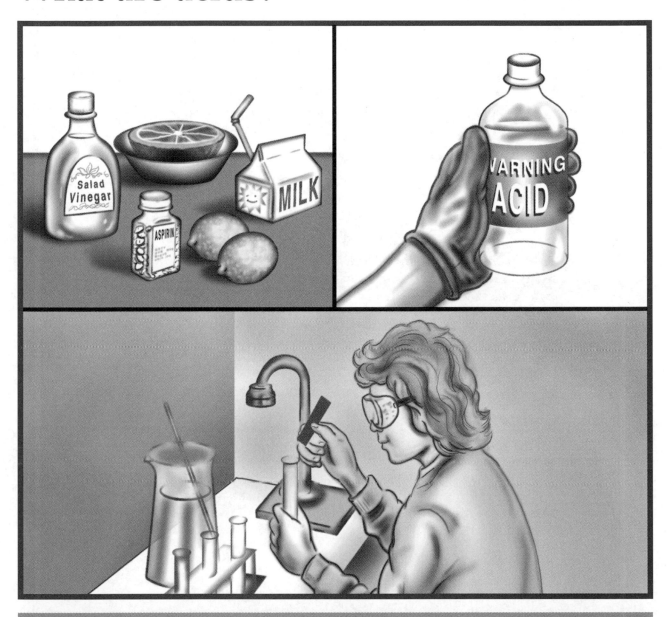

What are acids?

KEY TERMS

acid: substance that reacts with metals to release hydrogen

indicator: substance that changes color in acids and bases

LESSON 22 | What are acids?

The sour taste of the lemon juice tells us that it is an **acid**. Acids are special kinds of chemicals. They are common in everyday life. Some are helpful, others are harmful. There are some that are weak. Others are strong. Many acids are <u>dangerous</u> to touch or taste. You should <u>never</u> touch or taste an unknown acid.

Besides the sour taste that acids have, there are other tests for identifying them. Certain chemicals change color when acids are added.

Chemicals that change color are called **indicators** [IN-duh-kayt-urz].

An example of an indicator is a litmus paper. Litmus paper comes in two colors, red and blue.

- Acids turn blue litmus paper red. Acids do not change the color of red litmus paper.

- When acids mix with most metals, a chemical reaction takes place. Acids wear away most metals. Hydrogen gas is given off from this reaction.

TESTING FOR AN ACID

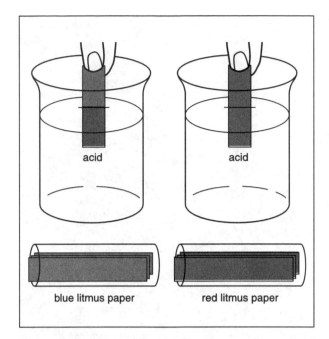

Acids turn blue litmus paper red.

Does the red litmus paper change color with acids? _____ no _____

Figure A

SOME COMMON ACIDS

The chart lists some common acids and their chemical formulas. It shows you what all acids have in common. All acids contain the element hydrogen (H+).

	ACID	CHEMICAL FORMULA	USES
1.	Acetic acid	$HC_2H_3O_2$	vinegar
2.	Boric acid	H_3BO_3	eyewash
3.	Carbonic acid	H_2CO_3	club soda
4.	Citric acid	$H_3C_6H_5O_7$	citrus fruits
5.	Hydrochloric acid	HCl	aids digestion
6.	Nitric acid	HNO_3	fertilizers
7.	Sulfuric acid	H_2SO_4	plastics

Figure B *Citrus fruits have an acid called citric acid.*

Figure C *Vinegar is acetic acid.*

Figure D *Sulfuric acid is used in car batteries.*

Figure E *Hydrochloric acid produced in the stomach helps in digestion.*

FILL IN THE BLANK

Complete each statement using a term or terms from the list below. Write your answers in the spaces provided. Some words may be used more than once.

never	acid	blue
vinegar	hydrochloric acid	red
litmus paper	hydrogen	citric
dangerous		

1. Lemons contain _____citric_____ acid.

2. _____Litmus paper_____ is a kind of indicator.

3. Acids turn _____blue_____ litmus paper red.

4. _____Red_____ litmus paper does not change color in acids.

5. When acids wear away metals, _____hydrogen_____ is given off.

6. Acetic acid is found in household _____vinegar_____ .

7. Your stomach produces _____hydrochloric acid_____ .

8. All acids contain the element _____hydrogen_____ .

9. Some acids are _____dangerous_____ to touch or taste.

10. You should _____never_____ touch or taste an unknown _____acid_____ .

TRUE OR FALSE

In the space provided, write "true" if the sentence is true. Write "false" if the sentence is false.

True 1. Litmus paper is an indicator.

False 2. Acids turn red litmus paper blue.

True 3. Acids contain hydrogen.

True 4. Acids wear away most metals.

False 5. Oxygen is given off when acids wear down metals.

WORD SCRAMBLE

Below are several scrambled words you have used in this Lesson. Unscramble the words and write your answers in the spaces provided.

1. CADI ACID

2. TRINOCDIA INDICATOR

3. SSTTE TESTS

4. SITLUM LITMUS

5. RUSO SOUR

REACHING OUT

Figure F

Sometimes when rain falls, it mixes with pollution particles in the air. An acid is formed.

Why might this be harmful? __Accept all logical responses. Likely responses include:__

the acid will react with and harm the objects that the rain falls upon.

What are bases?

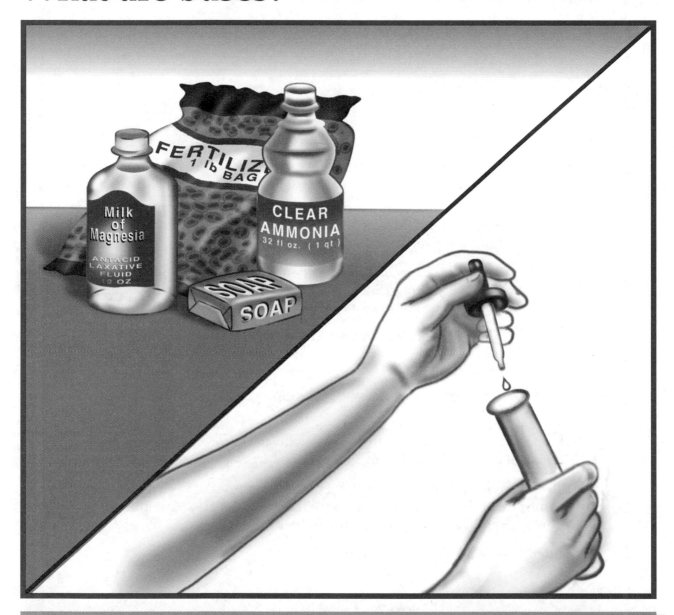

KEY TERMS

base: substance formed when metals react with water

phenolphthalein: an indicator that turns a deep pink color when a base is added

LESSON 23 | What are bases?

Bases are a group of chemicals that have certain common properties. Their properties are different from the properties of acids. Often they act opposite to the ways that acids act.

However, like acids, bases may be of different strengths. Some are very weak. Some are very strong. Some bases are dangerous to touch or taste. You should never touch or taste an unknown base.

Let us see how bases act with tests that we use to identify chemicals.

Bases have a bitter taste.

If you touch a harmless base, it will feel slippery. Acids do not have any special feel.

Bases act the opposite way from acids with indicators. Bases turn red litmus paper blue. They do not change blue litmus paper.

There is another indicator that helps us to identify bases. It is called phenolphthalein [fee-nohl-THAL-een]. This solution is clear in acids. But phenolphthalein turns deep pink in bases.

Unlike acids, bases do not wear away metals.

TESTING FOR A BASE

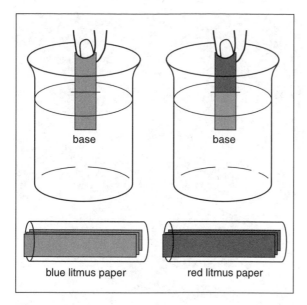

Figure A

Figure B

Bases turn red litmus paper blue. Blue litmus paper does not change color.

What happens to blue litmus paper in acids? _____ It stays blue. _____

Phenolphthalein turns deep pink in bases.

What happens to phenolphthalein in acids?

It is clear.

SOME COMMON BASES

The chart lists some common bases and their chemical formulas. It shows you what all bases have in common. All bases contain special groups of oxygen and hydrogen atoms called hydroxides (OH^-).

	BASE	CHEMICAL FORMULA	USES
1.	Potassium hydroxide	KOH	soap
2.	Magnesium hydroxide	$Mg(OH)_2$	milk of magnesia
3.	Calcium hydroxide	$Ca(OH)_2$	mortar
4.	Ammonium hydroxide	NH_4OH	ammonia
5.	Sodium hydroxide	$NaOH$	soap

Figure C *Ammonia is used in cleaning products.*

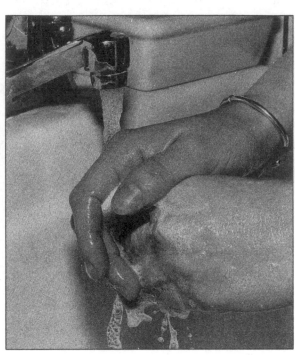

Figure D *Soap contains a base called lye.*

Figure E *Milk of magnesia is used to neutralize excess stomach acids.*

Figure F *Ammonium hydroxide is important in making fertilizers.*

Complete each statement using a term or terms from the list below. Write your answers in the spaces provided.

bitter	dangerous	opposite to
chemicals	do not change	pink
change	indicators	sour
lye		

1. Bases are a group of ____chemicals____ .

2. Bases often act ____opposite to____ the ways that acids act.

3. Both acids and bases can be ____dangerous____ .

4. Bases have a ____bitter____ taste.

5. Acids have a ____sour____ taste.

6. Bases ____change____ the color of red litmus paper.

7. Bases ____do not change____ the color of blue litmus paper.

8. Phenolphthalein turns ____pink____ in bases.

9. Phenolphthalein and litmus paper are ____indicators____ .

10. Soap contains a base called ____lye____ .

MATCHING

Match each term in Column A with its description in Column B. Write the correct letter in the space provided.

Column A	Column B
__c__ 1. red litmus paper	a) ammonia
__d__ 2. blue litmus paper	b) turns pink in bases
__b__ 3. phenolphthalein	c) turns blue in bases
__e__ 4. an acid	d) stays blue in bases
__a__ 5. a base	e) vinegar

TRUE OR FALSE

In the space provided, write "true" if the sentence is true. Write "false" if the sentence is false.

False	1.	Bases taste sour.
True	2.	Bases feel slippery.
False	3.	Bases turn blue litmus paper red.
True	4.	Bases turn red litmus paper blue.
True	5.	Phenolphthalein turns deep pink in bases.
False	6.	Bases wear away metals.
True	7.	Bases can be dangerous.
False	8.	Acids contain the OH^- groups.
True	9.	Acids contain the H^+ groups.
False	10.	All bases are strong.

REACHING OUT

Why are indicators useful? _Accept all logical responses. Likely responses include_ that indicators let us know if something is an acid or a base.

Acids and Bases

What happens when acids and bases are mixed?

$$HCl + Na(OH) \rightarrow NaCl + H_2O$$

KEY TERMS

neutral: neither acidic nor basic

neutralization: reaction between an acid and a base to produce a salt and water

LESSON 24 | What happens when acids and bases are mixed?

In a courtroom, a judge is not supposed to take sides. The judge is there to make sure that everything is fair for both sides. An umpire does the same thing in a baseball game. We say that people like judges and umpires are <u>neutral</u>.

In chemistry, a liquid is **neutral** if it is not an acid or a base. Take water, for example. Water is neutral. It is not an acid. It is not a base.

Acids and bases have definite properties. In many ways they are opposite. What happens if you mix an acid with a base?

When you mix an acid with a base, a chemical reaction takes place. The atoms from the acid and the base change the way they are linked up. New products are formed. These new products have their own properties. The properties are different from the properties of either acids or bases.

What do you get?

When you mix the right amounts of an acid and a base, you get a salt and water. The salt is dissolved in the water. It forms a salt solution. A salt solution is not an acid; it is not a base. It is neutral.

$$\text{ACID + BASE} \xrightarrow{\text{makes}} \text{A SALT + WATER}$$

The link-up of an acid and a base to form a salt and water is called **neutralization** [new-truh-li-ZAY-shun].

There are many kinds of acids. There are many kinds of bases. There are many kinds of salts. The salt you sprinkle on your food is just one kind of salt called sodium chloride. Its formula is NaCl. Different salts have different formulas.

MIXING AN ACID AND A BASE

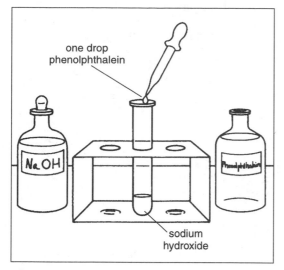

Figure A

The test tube in Figure A contains twenty drops of sodium hydroxide (NaOH).

One drop of phenolphthalein is added. The phenolphthalein turns deep pink.

This shows that sodium hydroxide (NaOH)

is _____ a base _____ .

an acid, a base

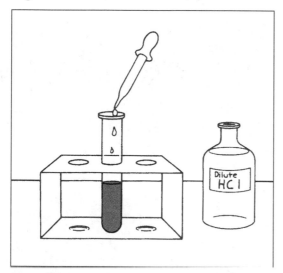

Figure B

A different dropper is used in Figure B to add fifteen drops of hydrochloric acid (HCl) —one drop at a time.

The solution stays pink.

This shows that the solution

_____ is still a base _____ .

is neutral, is an acid, is still a base

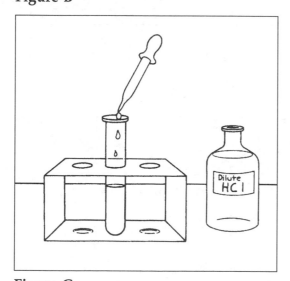

Figure C

More hydrochloric acid (HCl) is added — one drop at a time, until the pink disappears.

The loss of the pink color shows that the

solution is _____ no longer a base _____ .

an acid, no longer a base

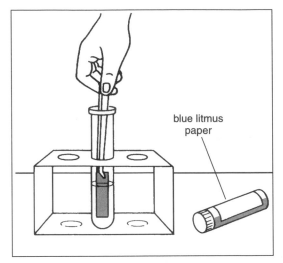

The solution is tested with blue litmus paper.

The blue litmus paper stays blue.

This shows that the solution is not

$$\underline{\hspace{3em} \text{an acid} \hspace{3em}}.$$
an acid, a base

Figure D

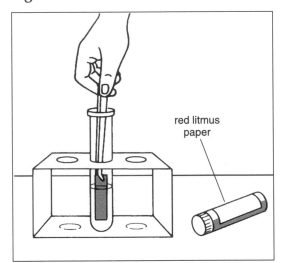

The solution is tested with red litmus paper.

The red litmus paper stays red.

This shows that the solution is not

$$\underline{\hspace{3em} \text{a base} \hspace{3em}}.$$
an acid, a base

Figure E

CONCLUSION

The mixture _____ is _____ neutral.
is, is not

Fill in the boxes to show what happened:

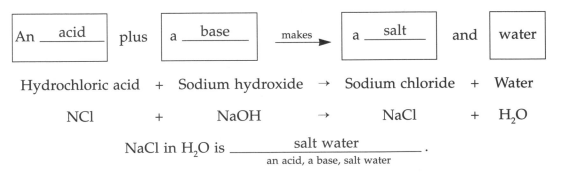

Hydrochloric acid + Sodium hydroxide → Sodium chloride + Water

NCl   +   NaOH   →   NaCl   + H_2O

NaCl in H_2O is _____ salt water _____.
an acid, a base, salt water

158

FILL IN THE BLANK

Complete each statement using a term or terms from the list below. Write your answers in the spaces provided. Some words may be used more than once.

water	a base	table
neutralization	many kinds	neutral
litmus paper	reaction	phenolphthalein
an acid	a salt	

1. Lemon juice is an example of _____ an acid _____ . Lye is an example of

    _____ a base _____ .

2. Any substance that is not an acid or a base is said to be _____ neutral _____ .

3. An example of a neutral liquid is _____ water _____ .

4. The mixing of an acid and a base causes a chemical _____ reaction _____ .

5. If we mix the right amounts of an acid and a base, we get _____ a salt _____ and

    _____ water _____ .

6. The chemical reaction between an acid and a base to produce a salt and water is

    called _____ neutralization _____ .

7. There are _____ many kinds _____ of salts.

8. The most common salt is _____ table _____ salt.

9. Salt water does not change the color of _____ litmus paper _____ or

    _____ phenolphthalein _____ .

10. Salt water is neither _____ an acid _____ nor _____ a base _____ . Salt water is

    _____ neutral _____ .

MATCHING

Match each term in Column A with its description in Column B. Write the correct letter in the space provided.

	Column A		Column B
a	1. HCl	a)	acid
c	2. NaOH	b)	water
b	3. H$_2$O	c)	base
e	4. NaCl	d)	indicator
d	5. phenolphthalein	e)	salt

159

TRUE OR FALSE

In the space provided, write "true" if the sentence is true. Write "false" if the sentence is false.

False **1.** An acid is neutral.

False **2.** A base is neutral.

True **3.** Water is neutral.

True **4.** There is only one formula for water.

False **5.** There is only one kind of salt.

True **6.** Salt water is neutral.

False **7.** If you mix an acid with a base, you get only water.

False **8.** Blue litmus paper changes to red in salt water.

True **9.** Red litmus paper stays red in salt water.

False **10.** Phenolphthalein turns pink in salt water.

REACHING OUT

When hydrochloric acid reacts with potassium hydroxide, potassium chloride is formed.

- The formula for hydrochloric acid is HCl.

- The formula for potassium hydroxide is KOH.

What is the formula for water? _____H_2O_____

What is the formula for potassium chloride? _____KCl_____

Why do some liquids conduct electricity?

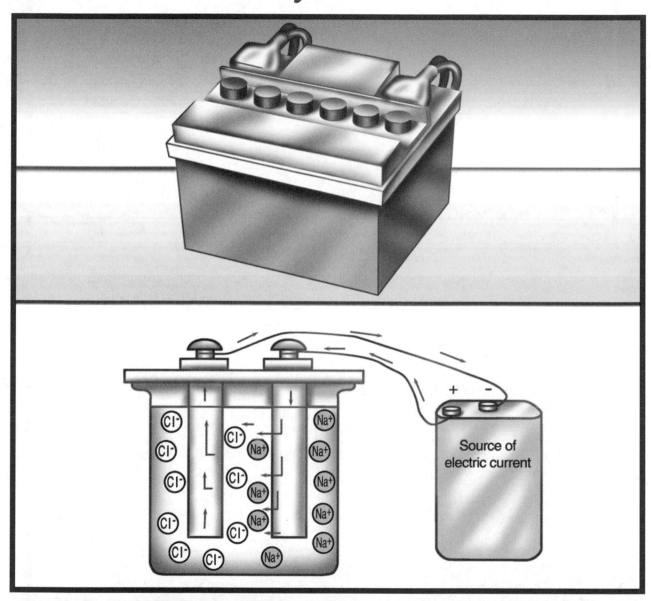

Source of electric current

KEY TERMS

ion: charged particle

electrolyte: substance that conducts an electric current when it is dissolved in water

LESSON 25 | Why do some liquids conduct electricity?

Solutions of acids, bases, and salts conduct electricity. Solid acids, bases, and salts do not. Neither do liquids like alcohol, sugar water, distilled water, and glycerine.

Why do liquid acids, bases, and salts conduct electricity? Scientists explain it this way.

Matter is made up of atoms. Sometimes atoms join together to form molecules. Most atoms and molecules have no electrical charge. They are neutral. The atoms of substances that are not acids, bases, or salts stay neutral. They stay neutral even when they dissolve.

Solutions of acids, bases, and salts do not stay neutral. These compounds are made of formula units instead of molecules. This is because of the way they are put together.

What happens to an acid, base, or salt when it dissolves?

When an acid, base, or salt dissolves, its atoms do not stay together. The atoms unlock. When they unlock, they do not stay neutral. They take on electrical charges. Some atoms have a positive (+) charge. Some have a negative (–) charge. Charged atoms are called **ions** [I-unz].

Ions let electricity pass through a solution. Solutions that have ions are called **electrolytes** [i-LEK-truh-lyts].

Liquid acids, bases, and salts form ions. That is why they conduct electricity.

Liquids such as alcohol, sugar water, distilled water, and glycerine do not form ions. That is why they do not conduct electricity. They are nonelectrolytes.

TESTING ELECTROLYTES

We can test whether a solution conducts electricity by using a battery and a light bulb. The bulb lights up if the liquid is an electrolyte.

Figure A

The brightness of the light tells if the electrolyte is strong or weak.

- A <u>bright</u> light means a <u>strong electrolyte</u> (good conductor).
- A <u>dim</u> light means a <u>weak electrolyte</u> (poor conductor).
- <u>No</u> light means a <u>nonelectrolyte</u> (nonconductor).

The chart below lists 10 liquids. They have been tested as in Figure A. The checks show how brightly the bulb lit up.

	Liquid	Light Brightness		
		Bright	**Dim**	**No Light**
1.	Sodium chloride (salt)	✔		
2.	Sugar			✔
3.	Boric acid		✔	
4.	Sodium hydroxide (base)	✔		
5.	Distilled water			✔
6.	Acetic acid		✔	
7.	Alcohol			✔
8.	Magnesium sulfate (salt)	✔		
9.	Glycerine			✔
10.	Carbonic acid		✔	

Answer these questions about the information on the chart.

1. List the electrolytes <u>Sodium chloride, Boric acid, Sodium hydroxide, Acetic</u>
   <u>acid, Magnesium sulfate, Carbonic acid</u>

   _____

2. **a)** Which are strong electrolytes? <u>Sodium chloride, Sodium hydroxide,</u>
   <u>Magnesium sulfate</u>

   _____

   b) How do you know? <u>The bulb lit up brightly.</u>

3. **a)** Which are weak electrolytes? <u>Boric acid, Acetic acid, Carbonic acid</u>

   _____

4. **a)** Which are nonelectrolytes? <u>Sugar, Distilled water, Alcohol, Glycerine</u>

   _____

   b) How do you know? <u>The bulb did not light up.</u>

5. Which groups of liquids let the bulb light up? <u>acids, bases, salts</u>

   _____

6. Which groups of liquids are electrolytes? <u>acids, bases, salts</u>

   _____

TRUE OR FALSE

In the space provided, write "true" if the sentence is true. Write "false" if the sentence is false.

<u>False</u>   **1.** A regular atom has a charge.

<u>True</u>   **2.** An ion has a charge.

<u>False</u>   **3.** Only positive ions have a charge.

<u>True</u>   **4.** Liquids that conduct electricity are called electrolytes.

<u>True</u>   **5.** Electrolytes contain ions.

<u>True</u>   **6.** An electrolyte contains plus and minus ions.

EXPLAINING IONIZATION

Let us see what happens in a salt solution.

Table salt has atoms of sodium (Na) and chlorine (Cl). One formula unit of salt has one atom of sodium linked to one atom of chlorine. Atoms of sodium and chlorine have no charge. Formula units of the solid salt NaCl have no charge.

NaCl in the solid state does not conduct electricity.

When NaCl dissolves, the sodium and chlorine atoms break away from each other. They take on electrical charges. The sodium takes on a positive charge. The chlorine takes on a negative charge.

The charged atoms are now called ions. Ions conduct electricity. Liquids that form ions are called electrolytes.

- Liquid acids, bases, and salts form ions.

- Liquid acids, bases, and salts are electrolytes.

- Liquid acids, bases, and salts conduct electricity.

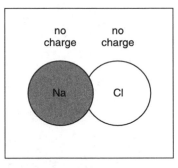

Figure B *One formula unit of salt in the solid state*

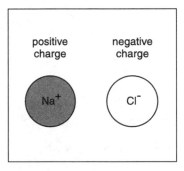

Figure C *One formula unit of salt in the ionized state*

FILL IN THE BLANK

Complete each statement using a term or terms from the list below. Write your answers in the spaces provided. Some words may be used more than once.

salts	electrolytes	negative
positive	no	atoms
ions	bases	conduct
acids		

1. Matter that is electrically neutral has _____no_____ charge.

2. Regular _____atoms_____ are electrically neutral.

3. Regular atoms have _____no_____ charge.

4. Atoms that have a charge are called _____ions_____ .

5. Some ions have a _____positive_____ charge; some have a _____negative_____ charge.

6. Atoms of _____acids_____ , _____bases_____ , and _____salts_____ form ions.

7. Ions _____conduct_____ electricity.

8. Solutions that conduct electricity are called _____electrolytes_____ .

9. Liquid _____acids_____ , _____bases_____ , and _____salts_____ are electrolytes.

10. Liquids like alcohol and distilled water do not form _____ions_____ . They are not _____electrolytes_____ .

MATCHING

Match each term in Column A with its description in Column B. Write the correct letter in the space provided.

	Column A		Column B
__d__	1. ion	a)	kinds of charges
__a__	2. positive and negative	b)	do not conduct electricity
__c__	3. electrolyte	c)	liquid that conducts electricity
__e__	4. regular atom	d)	charged atom or group of atoms
__b__	5. dry acids, bases, and salts	e)	has no charge

What are oxidation numbers?

$$Na^{+1} + Cl^{-1} \longrightarrow NaCl$$

$$H^{+1} \qquad O^{-2}$$

$$H_2 \qquad O_1$$

$$H_2O$$

KEY TERM

oxidation number: the number of electrons an atom can lend or borrow

LESSON 26 | What are oxidation numbers?

Atoms of metals link up with atoms of nonmetals. They form compounds. When a compound forms, the metal lends outer-ring electrons to the nonmetal. The nonmetal borrows the electrons.

How many electrons does an atom lend or borrow? It depends upon the atom. It also depends upon the compound being formed. Some atoms give up or take on more electrons than others. The number of electrons an atom can lend or borrow is called its **oxidation number**.

An oxidation number is a number with a plus (+) or minus (–) sign in front of it. The oxidation number is written next to the atom it describes, such as Al^{+3}, Mg^{+2}, Br^{-1}, and Se^{-2}.

The sign (+ or –) tells us whether the atom lends or borrows electrons.

- A <u>plus (+) sign</u> means that the atom <u>lends</u> electrons.

- A <u>minus (–) sign</u> means that the atom <u>borrows</u> electrons.

The number tells us <u>how many</u> electrons the atom lends or borrows.

Let's look at two oxidation numbers.

- Sodium has an oxidation number of +1 (Na^{+1}). This means that sodium can lend one electron.

- The oxidation number of oxygen is –2 (O^{-2}). Oxygen can borrow two electrons.

Metals have plus oxidation numbers. Metals lend electrons.

Nonmetals have minus oxidation numbers. Nonmetals borrow electrons.

A nonmetal will borrow enough electrons to complete its outer shell.

Many elements have more than one oxidation number. In fact, some elements have both plus and minus oxidation numbers. Sometimes they lend electrons. Sometimes they borrow electrons.

USING THE PERIODIC TABLE TO FIND OXIDATION NUMBERS

You can find the oxidation numbers of many elements by looking at the periodic table.

FINDING THE OXIDATION NUMBER OF A METAL

This is the simplest oxidation number to find. In many cases, the oxidation number of a metal is the same as the number of electrons in its outer shell.

A metal lends (loses) electrons. Therefore, its oxidation number is plus (+).

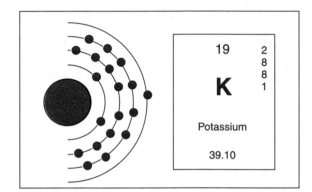

Figure A shows an example.

Potassium has 1 outer-shell electron.

Potassium lends this single electron.

The oxidation number of potassium is +1 (K^{+1}).

Figure A

FINDING THE OXIDATION NUMBER OF A NONMETAL

This is simple too. Here is what to do:

- Check the number of electrons in the outer shell.

- Figure out how many electrons that atom needs to make a stable outer shell (in most cases, 8 electrons). That number is the oxidation number.

A nonmetal will add, or borrow, these electrons. Therefore, its oxidation number is minus (–).

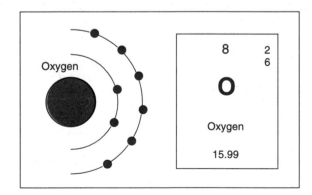

Figure B shows an example.

Oxygen has 6 outer-shell electrons.

Oxygen needs 2 more electrons to make its outer shell stable ($8 - 6 = 2$).

Oxygen will borrow (gain) these 2 electrons.

The oxidation number of oxygen is –2 (O^{-2}).

Figure B

Figure C

4	2
Be	2
Beryllium	
9.01	

1. How many outer-shell electrons does beryllium have? _____2_____

2. Beryllium is a ___metal___ .
   metal, nonmetal

3. Beryllium ___lends___ electrons.
   lends, borrows

4. How many electrons can beryllium lend? _____2_____

5. What is the oxidation number of beryllium? _____+2_____

Figure D

16	2
S	8
	6
Sulfur	
32.06	

6. a) How many outer-shell electrons does sulfur have? _____6_____

   b) Is this a stable shell? _____no_____

   c) How many electrons are needed to make a stable shell? _____2_____

7. Sulfur is a ___nonmetal___ .
   metal, nonmetal

8. Sulfur ___borrows___ electrons.
   lends, borrows

9. How many electrons can sulfur borrow? _____2_____

10. What is the oxidation number of sulfur? _____−2_____

WORKING WITH OXIDATION NUMBERS

Ten elements and their oxidation numbers are listed below. Study each one. Then fill in the chart. The first line has been filled in for you.

	Element	Symbol and oxidation number	Metal or nonmetal	Lends or borrows electrons?	Lends or borrows how many electrons?
1.	Oxygen	O^{-2}	Nonmetal	borrows	2
2.	Calcium	Ca^{+2}	Metal	lends	2
3.	Aluminum	Al^{+3}	Metal	lends	3
4.	Bromine	Br^{-1}	Nonmetal	borrows	1
5.	Nitrogen	N^{-3}	Nonmetal	borrows	3
6.	Zinc	Zn^{+2}	Metal	lends	2
7.	Lithium	Li^{+1}	Metal	lends	1
8.	Sulfur	S^{-2}	Nonmetal	borrows	2
9.	Phosphorus	P^{-3}	Nonmetal	borrows	3
10.	Silver	Ag^{+1}	Metal	lends	1

USING OXIDATION NUMBERS

You can use oxidation numbers to figure out the formula for any simple compound. All you need to know are the symbols and the oxidation numbers of the elements that make up the compound. JUST CRISSCROSS THE OXIDATION NUMBERS.

Water is made up of hydrogen (H) and oxygen (O). The oxidation number of hydrogen is +1 (H^{+1}). The oxidation number of oxygen is –2 (O^{-2}).

For example, this is how to write the formula for water:

Step 1 Write down the symbol of each element. List the element with the plus (+) oxidation number first.

$$H \quad O$$

Step 2 Write down the oxidation number of each element next to the element like this:

$$H^+ \quad O^{-2}$$

Step 3 Crisscross the <u>numbers</u> in the oxidation number only. Leave out the signs.

$$H^{+1} \quad O^{-2}$$
$$H_2 \quad O_1 = H_2O_1$$

One molecule of water, then, contains 2 atoms of hydrogen and 1 atom of oxygen.

In a final formula, we do not write any 1's. So the formula for water is **H_2O**.

Table salt is made up of atoms of sodium (Na) and chlorine (Cl). The oxidation number of sodium is +1 (Na^{+1}). The oxidation number of chlorine is –1 (Cl^{-1}).

- Write it down $Na^{+1}Cl^{-1}$

- Cross over the numbers. $Na^{+1}Cl^{-1}$
$$Na_1 \quad Cl_1$$

- Cancel out the ones. $Na_{\cancel{1}} \; Cl_{\cancel{1}}$

The formula for table salt is **NaCl**.

Table salt is sodium chloride. One formula unit of sodium chloride has 1 atom of sodium and 1 atom of chlorine. Altogether one formula unit of salt contains 2 atoms.

What do you do if both oxidation numbers (not the signs) are the same? This is the case when magnesium and oxygen combine.

$$Mg^{+2}O^{-2}$$
$$Mg_2 \; O_2 = Mg_2O_2$$

Cancel out both numbers like this: **$Mg_{\cancel{2}}O_{\cancel{2}}$**

The formula, then, is **MgO**.

There are some compounds where the numbers are not canceled out, but these compounds will not be covered in this book.

WRITING FORMULAS

Work these out by yourself. It's easy! Just do one step at a time.

Calcium (Ca) links up with iodine (I) to form a compound called calcium iodide.
The oxidation number of calcium is +2 (Ca^{+2}). The oxidation number of iodine is –1 (I^{-1}).

1. Write down each element and its oxidation number. (Remember, the + oxidation number comes first.)

   1. $Ca^{+2} \ I^{-1}$

2. Cross over the numbers.

   2. $Ca_1 \ I_2$

3. Cancel out numbers. (Skip if not needed.)

   3. $Ca_{\cancel{1}} \ I_2$

4. Write the formula.

   4. CaI_2

5. What is the name of this compound? __calcium iodide__

6. One formula unit of calcium iodide has _____one_____ atom(s) of calcium and
   _____two_____ atom(s) of iodine.

7. Altogether, how many atoms does one formula unit of calcium iodide have? __three__

Gold and sulfur combine to form the compound gold sulfide.
The oxidation number of gold is +1 (Au^{+1}). The oxidation number of sulfur is –2 (S^{-2}).

8. Write down each element and its oxidation number.

   8. $Au^{+1} \ S^{-2}$

9. Cross over numbers.

   9. $Au_2 \ S_1$

10. Cancel out numbers. (Skip if not needed.)

    10. $Au_2 \ S_{\cancel{1}}$

11. Write the formula.

    11. Au_2S

12. What is the name of this compound? __gold sulfide__

13. One formula unit of gold sulfide has _____two_____ atom(s) of gold and
    _____one_____ atom(s) of sulfur.

14. Altogether, how many atoms does one formula unit of gold sulfide have? __three__

FILL IN THE BLANK

Complete each statement using a term or terms from the list below. Write your answers in the spaces provided. Some words may be used more than once.

lend	oxidation number	number
more than one	borrow	complete outer shell
how many	loses	compounds
+ or – sign	gains	

1. Metals link up with nonmetals to form ___compounds___ .

2. When forming compounds, metals ___lend___ electrons. Nonmetals ___borrow___ electrons.

3. An atom's ___oxidation number___ tells how many electrons the atom can lend or borrow.

4. An oxidation number is written as a ___number___ with a ___+ or – sign___ in front of it.

5. The number tells us ___how many___ electrons an atom gains or loses.

6. The sign tells us whether the atom will ___lend___ or ___borrow___ electrons.

7. An atom with a plus (+) oxidation number lends electrons. Another way of saying this is: An atom with a plus oxidation number ___loses___ electrons.

8. An atom with a minus (–) oxidation number borrows electrons. Another way of saying this is: An atom with a minus oxidation number ___gains___ electrons.

9. A nonmetal will borrow enough electrons to give a ___complete outer shell___ .

10. Many elements have ___more than one___ oxidation number.

MATCHING

Match each term in Column A with its description in Column B. Write the correct letter in the space provided.

	Column A		Column B
__c__	1. compound	**a)**	tells how many electrons an atom can lend or borrow
__e__	2. 2 or 8 outer-shell electrons	**b)**	lends electrons
__a__	3. oxidation number	**c)**	at least one metal and one nonmetal
__b__	4. + oxidation number atom	**d)**	borrows electrons
__d__	5. – oxidation number atom	**e)**	complete outer shell

COMPLETE THE CHART

Write the correct formulas in the spaces below. Three formulas have been written for you.

NONMETALS

	Cl^{-1}	S^{-2}	O^{-2}	I^{-1}	Br^{-1}
H^{+1}	1. HCl	2. H_2S	3. H_2O	4. HI	5. HBr
Al^{+3}	6. $AlCl_3$	7. Al_2S_3	8. Al_2O_3	9. AlI_3	10. AlI_3
Ca^{+2}	11. $CaCl_2$	12. CaS	13. CaO	14. CaI_2	15. $CaBr_2$
Cu^{+1}	16. $CuCl$	17. Cu_2S	18. Cu_2O	19. CuI	20. $CuBr$
Mg^{+2}	21. $MgCl_2$	22. MgS	23. MgO	24. MgI_2	25. $MgBr_2$
Na^{+1}	26. $NaCl$	27. Na_2S	28. Na_2O	29. NaI	30. $NaBr$

METALS

REACHING OUT

Oxidation numbers can help you find a formula. It goes the other way too. A formula can help you find the oxidation number of the elements in a compound.

For example, NiI_2 is the formula for nickel iodide. The formula tells us that:

- The oxidation number of nickel is +2. (Remember, the metal always goes first—and a metal has a positive (+) oxidation number.)

- The oxidation number of iodine is –1.

Six compounds are listed below. Figure out the oxidation number of the elements in each compound. The first one has been done for you.

	Formula	Atoms and Their Oxidation Numbers	
1.	CaF_2	Ca^{+2}	F^{-1}
2.	KBr	K^{+1}	Br^{-1}
3.	Mg_3N_2	Mg^{+2}	N^{-3}
4.	CCl_4	C^{+4}	Cl^{-1}
5.	H_2S	H^{+1}	S^{-2}
6.	$FeCl_3$	Fe^{+3}	Cl^{-1}

What is a polyatomic ion?

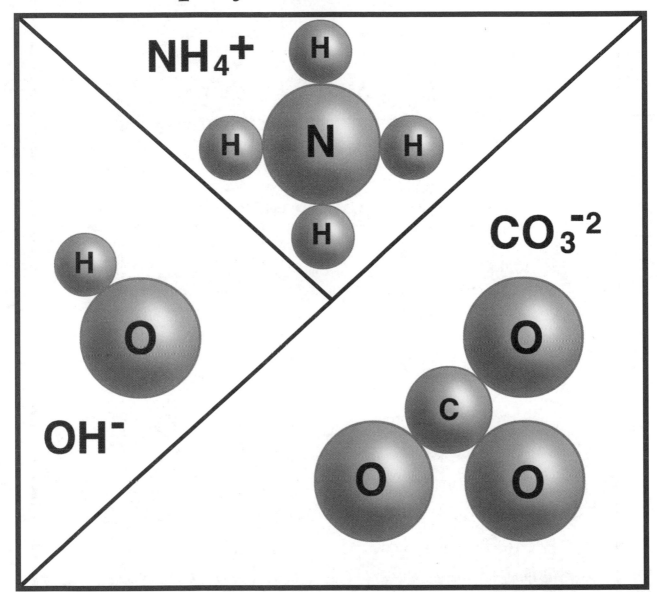

KEY TERMS

polyatomic ion: group of atoms that acts as a single atom

subscript: number written to the lower right of a chemical symbol

LESSON 27 | What is a polyatomic ion?

Many friends are "extra" good friends. They get together very often. And then they seem to act like one person.

Certain elements are like that. They "get together" whenever possible. And then they act as if they were one atom.

A group of atoms that behaves like a single atom is called a **polyatomic** [PAHL-i-uh-tahm-ik] **ion**. A polyatomic ion has its own oxidation number.

Eight common polyatomic ions along with their oxidation numbers are listed on the facing page. All the common polyatomic ions have a minus oxidation number except one. The ammonium polyatomic ion (NH_4) has a +1 oxidation number $(NH_4)^{+1}$.

The polyatomic ions in the chart are listed within parentheses like (OH). Parentheses are not always needed. For example, the (OH) in the formula Na(OH) does not need parentheses. It can be written as NaOH.

Parentheses are always needed when a subscript follows a polyatomic ion. Take this formula for example—$Ca(OH)_2$. The small 2 after the OH is a **subscript**. It means that one formula unit of this compound has two hydroxyl (OH) polyatomic ions.

How do you find the formula for a simple compound that has one or even two polyatomic ions? It's simple. Just crisscross the oxidation numbers—just as you did in the last lesson.

Here are two examples.

1. $Ca^{+2} + (CO_3)^{-2}$

   $Ca_2(CO_3)_2$ (cancel out the 2's)

The final formula is $Ca(CO_3)$ or $CaCO_3$. Either one may be used. The name for this compound is calcium carbonate.

2. $(NH_4)^{+1} + (PO_4)^{-3}$

   $(NH_4)_3(PO_4)_1$ (cancel out the 1)

The final formula is $(NH_4)_3PO_4$. The name for this compound is ammonium phosphate.

UNDERSTANDING POLYATOMIC IONS

Polyatomic Ion	Formula and Oxidation Number	Polyatomic Ion	Formula and Oxidation Number
Ammonium	$(NH_4)^{+1}$	Carbonate	$(CO_3)^{-2}$
Bicarbonate	$(HCO_3)^{-1}$	Sulfite	$(SO_3)^{-2}$
Hydroxide	$(OH)^{-1}$	Sulfate	$(SO_4)^{-2}$
Nitrate	$(NO_3)^{-1}$	Phosphate	$(PO_4)^{-3}$

The chart above shows eight common polyatomic ions.

Now look at the chart below. The names of the eight polyatomic ions are listed in Column A.

Do the following:

- In Column B, write the formula of each polyatomic ion.
- In Column C, list the elements that make up each polyatomic ions and the number of atoms of each element.
- In Column D, list the oxidation number of each polyatomic ion.

The first one has been completed for you.

	A	B	C	D
	Polyatomic Ion	Formula	Elements and Number of Atoms of Each	Oxidation Number
1.	Sulfate	SO_4	Sulfur — 1 atom Oxygen — 4 atoms	-2
2.	Bicarbonate	HCO_3	Hydrogen — 1 atom Carbon — 1 atom Oxygen — 3 atoms	-1
3.	Nitrate	NO_3	Nitrogen — 1 atom Oxygen — 3 atoms	-1
4.	Ammonium	NH_4	Nitrogen — 1 atom Hydrogen — 4 atoms	$+1$
5.	Phosphate	PO_4	Phosphorus — 1 atom Oxygen — 4 atoms	-3
6.	Carbonate	CO_3	Carbon — 1 atom Oxygen — 3 atoms	-2
7.	Hydroxide	OH	Oxygen — 1 atom Hydrogen — 1 atom	-1
8.	Sulfite	SO_3	Sulfur — 1 atom Oxygen — 3 atoms	-2

NAMING COMPOUNDS

Eight compounds are listed in the chart below. Each one contains at least one polyatomic atom. Name each compound. Choose from the list below.

calcium carbonate	sodium sulfate
ammonium nitrate	ammonium chloride
potassium hydroxide	silver nitrate
copper nitrate	ammonium hydroxide

	Formula	Name
1.	$AgNO_3$	Silver nitrate
2.	KOH	Potassium hydroxide
3.	NH_4Cl	Ammonium chloride
4.	$CaCO_3$	Calcium carbonate
5.	$Cu(NO_3)_2$	Copper nitrate
6.	NH_4OH	Ammonium hydroxide
7.	NH_4NO_3	Ammonium nitrate
8.	Na_2SO_4	Sodium sulfate

WRITING FORMULAS

Write the correct formulas in the chart below. Two formulas have been written for you.

Remember: The plus oxidation number goes first. Then crisscross the oxidation numbers.

For example: $K^{+1} + (PO_4)^{-3}$

$K_3(PO_4)_1$

	$(OH)^{-1}$	$(NO_3)^{-1}$	$(PO_4)^{-3}$	$(HCO_3)^{-1}$	$(SO_4)^{-2}$
K^{+1}	1. KOH	2. KNO_3	3. $K_3(PO_4)$	4. $KHCO_3$	5. K_2SO_4
Mg^{+2}	6. $Mg(OH)_2$	7. $Mg(NO_3)_2$	8. $Mg_3(PO_4)_2$	9. $Mg(HCO_3)_2$	10. $MgSO_4$
H^{+1}	11. H_2O	12. HNO_3	13. H_3PO_4	14. H_2CO_3	15. H_2SO_4

What is a polyvalent element?

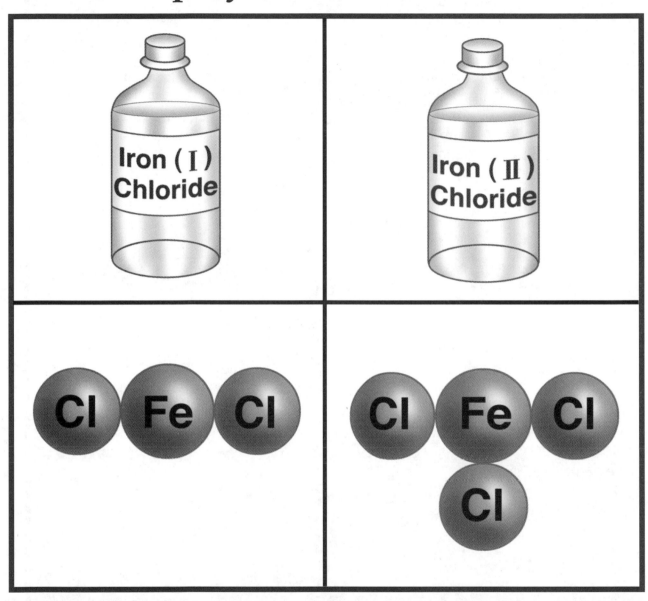

KEY TERM

polyvalent: having more than one oxidation number

LESSON 28 | What is a polyvalent element?

All elements have an oxidation number. Many elements have more than one oxidation number. Elements with more than one oxidation number are called **polyvalent** [pahl-i-VAY-lunt]. Many elements are polyvalent. Iron (Fe), for example, has an oxidation number of +2 (Fe^{+2}). Iron can also have an oxidation number of +3 (Fe^{+3}).

A polyvalent metal can form more than one kind of compound with the same nonmetal.

For example, iron (Fe) combines with chlorine (Cl^{-1}). The compound that forms can be either $FeCl_2$ or $FeCl_3$. Which one? It depends upon the oxidation number of the iron.

If iron with an oxidation number of +2 (Fe^{+2}) takes part in the reaction we get $FeCl_2$.

This compound is also called iron (II) chloride. The Roman numeral tells us the oxidation number of a polyvalent metal. Iron (II) means that the oxidation number of iron in this compound is +2.

$FeCl_2$ is also called FERROUS chloride. The *ferr-* part comes from *ferre,* the Latin word for iron. The *-ous* ending tells us that iron with the lower oxidation number took part in the reaction.

If iron with an oxidation number of +3 (Fe^{+3}) takes part in the reaction we get $FeCl_3$.

This compound is also called iron (III) chloride. What does iron (III) mean?

$FeCl_3$ is also called FERRIC chloride. The *-ic* ending tells us that iron with the higher oxidation number took part in the reaction.

WORKING WITH POLYVALENT ELEMENTS

The chart below shows five elements that are polyvalent. It shows the different oxidation numbers and the names that their compounds have.

OXIDATION NUMBERS OF METALS

Metal	Lower Oxidation Number	Name	Higher Oxidation Number	Name
Iron	Fe^{+2}	iron (II) ferrous	Fe^{+3}	iron (III) ferric
Mercury	Hg^{+1}	mercury (I) mercurous	Hg^{+2}	mercury (II) mercuric
Copper	Cu^{+1}	copper (I) cuprous	Cu^{+2}	copper (II) cupric
Gold	Au^{+1}	gold (I) aurous	Au^{+3}	gold (III) auric
Tin	Sn^{+2}	tin (II) stannous	Sn^{+4}	tin (IV) stannic

1. How many oxidation numbers does each of these elements have? _____ two _____

2. The name of each lower oxidation number compound ends with _____ ous _____ .
   -ous, -ic

3. The name of each higher oxidation number compounds ends with _____ ic _____ .
   -ous, -ic

In a compound, "ferr-" means iron. Which elements do these stand for?

4. stann- _____ tin _____ 5. cupr- _____ copper _____ 6. aur- _____ gold _____

Write the symbols and valences on the chart below. The first one has been done for you.

	Element	Symbol	Oxidation Numbers	
7.	Iron	Fe	+2	+3
8.	Tin	Sn	+2	+4
9.	Gold	Au	+1	+3
10.	Mercury	Hg	+1	+2
11.	Copper	Cu	+1	+2

WRITING FORMULAS

Write the formula for each combination. Then answer the questions.

1. a) $Fe^{+2} + I^{-1} \longrightarrow$

FeI_2

    b) The name of this compound is _____ferrous_____ iodide.
                                                  ferrous, ferric

2. a) $Hg^{+2} + Br^{-1} \longrightarrow$

$HgBr_2$

    b) The name of this compound is _____mercuric_____ bromide.
                                        mercurous, mercuric

3. a) $Sn^{+2} + F^{-1} \longrightarrow$

SnF_2

    b) The name of this compound is _____stannous_____ fluoride.
                                        stannous, stannic

2. a) $Cu^{+1} + S^{-2} \longrightarrow$

Cu_2S

    b) The name of this compound is _____cuprous_____ sulfide.
                                        cuprous, cupric

REACHING OUT

Which compound on this page is found in a familiar household product?

_____stannous fluoride_____

What is another name for this compound?

_____tin (II) fluoride_____

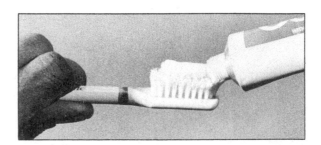

Figure A

What is formula mass?

23 + 35 = 58

Na + Cl → Na Cl

KEY TERMS

formula mass: sum of the mass numbers of all the atoms in a molecule or formula unit

coefficient: number that shows how many molecules of a substance are involved in a chemical reaction

LESSON 29 | What is formula mass?

Every compound has a formula. For example, H_2O is the formula for water. NaCl is the formula for table salt. $C_{12}H_{22}O_{11}$ is the formula for table sugar.

Compounds are made of atoms. Atoms have mass. Therefore, compounds have mass.

If we add up the mass of all the atoms in a compound, we find the mass of one molecule or formula unit of that compound.

The mass of one molecule or formula unit of a compound is called its **formula mass.** It also is called its molecular mass.

Let's look at an example.

How to find the formula mass of iron (III) oxide (Fe_2O_3):

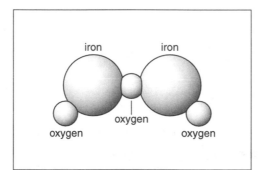

One formula unit of ferric oxide (Fe_2O_3) has 2 atoms of iron and 3 atoms of oxygen.

Element	Number of atoms		Atomic mass rounded off (mass of one atom)	Total mass of atoms
Iron	2	×	56	112
Oxygen	3	×	16	48

FORMULA MASS (mass of one formula unit of Fe_2O_3) = 160

WORKING WITH FORMULA MASSES

Find the formula (molecular) mass of each compound that follows. Look up the symbol names and atomic masses. (You probably know the names of most of these symbols.)

1.   Sulfuric acid H_2SO_4

Element	Number of atoms		Atomic mass	Total mass of atoms
Hydrogen	2	×	1	2
Sulfur	1	×	32	32
Oxygen	4	×	16	64

Formula mass = _____98_____

2.   Sucrose (table sugar) $C_{12}H_{22}O_{11}$

Element	Number of atoms		Atomic mass	Total mass of atoms
Carbon	12	×	12	144
Hydrogen	22	×	1	22
Oxygen	11	×	16	176

Formula mass = _____342_____

THE INSIDE STORY

Now let's try slightly more difficult compounds. (You will find that they are not really more difficult.) How do you handle a compound with a polyatomic ion? Formula units with polyatomic ions often have a part in parentheses and this part is followed by a subscript. $Ca(NO_3)_2$ (calcium nitrate) is an example.

Step 1   Find the number of atoms of each element.

The calcium **Ca** is <u>outside</u> the parentheses. No special figuring is needed. This formula has one atom of calcium.

The nitrate $(NO_3)_2$ needs some very easy figuring. Simply multiply the number of atoms of each element within the parentheses by the subscript ($_2$).

So we have

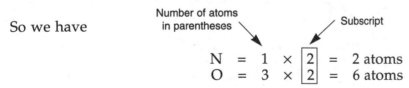

$$N = 1 \times \boxed{2} = 2 \text{ atoms}$$
$$O = 3 \times \boxed{2} = 6 \text{ atoms}$$

Step 2   Now we can find the formula mass.

Element	Number of atoms	Atomic mass	Total mass of atoms
Calcium	1	40	40
Nitrogen	2	14	28
Oxygen	6	16	96

Formula Mass of one formula unit of $Ca(NO_3)_2$ =   164

WORKING WITH COMPOUNDS WITH PARENTHESES

Five formulas are given. Figure out the number of atoms of each element.

1. $Fe(NO_3)_2$ Fe _____1_____   **2.** $AL_2(SO_4)_3$ Al _____2_____

　　　　　　　　N _____2_____　　　　　　　　　　　　S _____3_____

　　　　　　　　O _____6_____　　　　　　　　　　　　O _____12_____

Now that you know how to handle parentheses and subscripts, figure out the formula mass of each formula listed below. Find the names of the elements in the periodic table at the end of the book.

3. $Ca(OH)_2$

Element	Number of atoms	Atomic mass	Total mass of atoms
Calcium	1	40	40
Oxygen	2	16	32
Hydrogen	2	1	2

Formula mass = _____74_____

4. $Hg(SCN)_2$ (S, C, and N are separate elements. Naturally! Each one is a capital letter.)

Element	Number of atoms	Atomic mass	Total mass of atoms
Mercury	2	200	400
Sulfur	2	32	64
Carbon	2	12	24
Nitrogen	2	14	28

Formula mass = _____516_____

5. $Mg(C_7H_5O_3)_2$

Element	Number of of atoms	Atomic mass	Total mass of atoms
Magnesium	1	24	24
Carbon	14	12	168
Hydrogen	10	1	10
Oxygen	6	16	96

Formula mass = _____298_____

WHAT DOES THE NUMBER IN FRONT MEAN?

Sometimes you see a compound or a symbol that has a number in front of it. What does this mean?

What does the 2 mean in 2Na or NaCl? What does the 3 mean in $3H_2$?

The number in front tells you how many atoms or molecules there are. You multiply each kind of atom by this number. The number in front is called a **coefficient** [koh-uh-FISH-unt]. Let's look at some examples:

| 2Na | 2 Na means 2 atoms of sodium. |

| 2NaCl | 2NaCl means two formula units of NaCl. That means two atoms of sodium and two atoms of chlorine. |

| $3H_2$ | Here we must multiply the **3** $\times$ 2. There are 6 atoms of hydrogen. |

| $3H_2O$ | There are still 6 atoms of hydrogen. But we also have oxygen. $3 \times 1 = 3$ atoms of oxygen. |

Now let's see how to handle a compound that has both parentheses and a large coefficient.

| $2Ca(NO_3)_2$ | The **2** means two formula units of $Ca(NO_3)_2$. |

How many atoms of each element does this mean? We must multiply the number of each kind of atom by 2.

Ca $1 \times 2 = 2$ atoms

N   1 $\times$ (2) $\times$ (2) $=$ 4 atoms

| Subscript | Coefficient |

O   3 $\times$ (2) $\times$ (2) $=$ 12 atoms

An important thing to remember!

A coefficient in front of an element or a compund goes <u>only</u> with that element or compound. A plus (+) or an arrow ($\rightarrow$) tells us where the value of the coefficient ends. For example:

$$4Fe + 3O_2 \quad \rightarrow \quad 2Fe_2O_3$$

- The 4 in front of the Fe goes only with the Fe.
- The 3 in front of the O_2 goes only with the O_2.
- But the 2 in front of Fe_2O_3 goes with the Fe_2 <u>and</u> the O_3. They are part of the same molecule.

LET'S JUST COUNT

Count the number of atoms in each of the following:

1. $2Ba(OH)_2$ Ba   2

                 O   4

                 H   4

2. $4Al_2(SO_4)_3$ Al   8

                   S   12

                   O   48

3. $3Ba(OH)_2$ Ba   3

                 O   6

                 H   6

4. $2Mg(C_7H_5O_3)_2$ Mg   2

                   C   28

                   H   20

                   O   12

NOW BACK TO MASSES

Now you know how to handle formulas that have both parentheses and numbers in front. How do we figure masses for these formulas?

Simple, you have already learned that the formula mass of $Ca(NO_3)_2$ is 164. This means that one formula unit has a mass of 164.

What is the mass of $2Ca(NO_3)_2$? Easy! Just multiply the formula mass by 2.

Mass of $2Ca(NO_3)_2$: $2 \times 164 =$ 328   = FORMULA MASS

The formula mass of $Ba(OH)_2$ is 171. Figure the mass of each of the following:

1. $2Ba(OH)_2$ 342

2. $3Ba(OH)_2$ 513

The formula mass of $Pb(NO_3)_2$ is 331. Figure the mass of each of the following:

3. $2Pb(NO_3)_2$ 662

4. $4Pb(NO_3)_2$ 1,324

REACHING OUT

1. Find the formula mass of this compound: $Fe(NH_4)_2 (SO_4)_2$.

                                    284

2. Find the mass of the following: $2Al_2(SO_3)_3$

                                    588

What is a chemical equation?

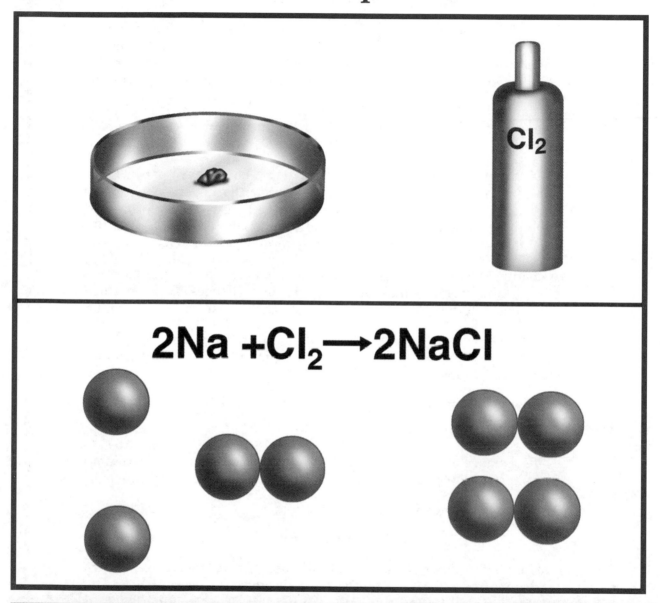

KEY TERMS

physical change: change in matter that does not produce any new products

chemical change: change in matter that produces new products

chemical equation: set of symbols and formulas that describes a chemical change

reactant: a substance that takes part in a chemical reaction (change)

product: a substance that is produced in a chemical reaction (change)

LESSON 30 | What is a chemical equation?

You may tear a sheet of paper into tiny pieces, but you still have paper. Each piece is still paper no matter how small. The way the atoms are linked together has not changed. No new products have been formed. The properties of the paper have not changed. Neither has its formula.

A change like tearing paper is called a **physical change**. In a physical change, only the appearance of a substance changes. The chemical makeup does not change.

What happens when you burn paper? You no longer have paper. Paper is a compound made up mostly of carbon and hydrogen. When paper burns, it links up with oxygen from the air. Three products form—ash, water, and carbon dioxide. When paper burns, there is a change in the way atoms link together. New products form. Properties change.

A change like burning paper is called a **chemical change**. In a chemical change, the chemical makeup of a substance changes. New products form. Each product has its own properties. Each one has its own formula.

A chemical change is caused by a chemical reaction. The "story" of a chemical reaction is called a **chemical equation**. A chemical equation shows two things:

- which substance(s) we start out with

- which substance(s) we end up with

The substance or substances we start out with are called the **reactants**. The substance or substances we end up with are called the **products**.

This is an example of a chemical equation:

$$Fe + S \rightarrow FeS$$

This equation describes the chemical reaction that takes place when a mixture of iron (Fe) and sulfur (S) is heated. The Fe and S are the reactants. The FeS (iron sulfide) is the product. The arrow means "produces" or "yields."

The properties of iron sulfide are different from those of iron or sulfur.

In any chemical equation
—the reactants are on the left side of the arrow
—the products are on the right side of the arrow.

Figure A *Sodium chloride (NaCl)*

Table salt (NaCl) is also called sodium chloride. It is a white solid. Your body contains this salt. It is necessary for life.

Figure B *Sodium (Na)*

Sodium (Na) is a very dangerous solid. It can explode in water.

Swallowing sodium can cause death.

Figure C *Chlorine (Cl)*

Chlorine (Cl) is a deadly greenish-yellow gas. If you inhale enough of this gas, it could be fatal.

Table salt (NaCl) can be melted. If an electric current passes through melted sodium chloride, a chemical reaction takes place. This is the chemical equation for this reaction.

$$2NaCl \rightarrow 2Na + Cl_2$$

Answer these questions.

1. This reaction has one reactant. Name that reactant. __sodium chloride (NaCl)__

2. The reactant in its natural state is a _____solid_____ .
   <small>solid, liquid, gas</small>

3. The reactant _____is not_____ dangerous.
   <small>is, is not</small>

4. Name the products. ___Sodium (Na)___ ___Chloride (Cl)___

5. What is the state of sodium? _____solid_____

6. Is sodium dangerous? _____yes_____

7. Are the properties of sodium the same as the properties of sodium chloride? __no__

8. What is the state of chlorine? _____gas_____

9. Is chlorine dangerous? _____yes_____

10. Are the properties of chlorine the same as the properties of sodium chloride? __no__

11. In a chemical reaction, properties _____do_____ change.
    <small>do, do not</small>

12. Name the kinds of atoms on the reactant side of this equation. ___Na and Cl___

13. Name the kinds of atoms on the product side. ___Na___ ___Cl___

14. The kinds of atoms on the reactant side _____are_____ the same as the atoms on the resultant side.
    <small>are, are not</small>

15. Are they in the same form? _____no_____

16. The atoms in the reactant are part of ___a compound___ .
    <small>a compound, two elements</small>

17. The atoms in the product are part of ___two elements___ .
    <small>a compound, two elements</small>

18. The arrangement of the atoms _____has_____ changed.
    <small>has, has not</small>

19. In this reaction, atoms have ___separated___ .
    <small>separated, linked up</small>

20. In a chemical reaction, the arrangement of the elements _____does_____ change.
    <small>does, does not</small>

PRODUCT OR REACTANT?

Five chemical equations are given below. Below each equation you will find the name of each substance in this equation. For each chemical equation:

- Write reactant next to each substance that is a reactant.

- Write product next to each substance that is a product.

1. $Zn + FeSO_4 \rightarrow ZnSO_4 + Fe$

   Zinc sulfate ____product____   Iron ____product____

   Zinc ____reactant____   Iron sulfate ____reactant____

2. $4HCl + MnO_2 \rightarrow MnCl_2 + 2H_2O + Cl_2$

   Chlorine ____product____

   Manganese chloride ____product____

   Manganese dioxide ____reactant____

   Water ____product____

   Hydrochloric acid (Hydrogen chloride) ____reactant____

3. $H_2SO_4 + BaCl_2 \rightarrow 2HCl + BaSO_4$

   Barium chloride ____reactant____

   Hydrochloric acid (hydrogen chloride) ____product____

   Barium sulfate ____product____

   Sulfuric acid (hydrogen sulfate) ____reactant____

4. $Br_2 + 2KI \rightarrow 2KBr + I_2$

   Potassium bromide ____product____   Iodine ____product____

   Bromine ____reactant____   Potassium iodide ____reactant____

5. $2ZnS + 3O_2 \rightarrow 2ZnO + 2SO_2$

   Oxygen ____reactant____   Sulfur dioxide ____product____

   Zinc oxide ____product____   Zinc sulfide ____reactant____

FILL IN THE BLANK

Complete each statement using a term or terms from the list below. Write your answers in the spaces provided.

products	right	physical
chemical equation	take part	yields
new	chemical	reaction
arrow	reactants	left

1. A change in which no new products are formed is called a ___physical___ change.

2. A change in which new products are formed is called a ___chemical___ change.

3. Another way of saying "chemical change" is "chemical ___reaction___."

4. A set of symbols and formulas that describes a chemical reaction is called a ___chemical equation___.

5. A chemical equation tells which substances ___take part___ in a chemical reaction. It also tells which ___new___ substances are formed.

6. The substances that take part in a chemical reaction are called the ___reactants___.

7. The new substances that form in a chemical reaction are called the ___products___.

8. In a chemical equation, the reactants are on the ___left___ side. The products are on the ___right___ side.

9. In a chemical reaction, the reactants and products are separated by an ___arrow___.

10. The arrow means "produces" or "___yields___."

REACHING OUT

Sodium hydroxide reacts with hydrochloric acid (hydrogen chloride) to produce sodium chloride (table salt) and water. Write the equation that shows this reaction.

$$NaOH + HCl \rightarrow NaCl + H_2O$$

Lesson

Does a chemical reaction destroy matter?

KEY TERM

Law of Conservation of Matter: scientific statement that says that a chemical reaction does not destroy or create matter

LESSON 31 | Does a chemical reaction destroy matter?

In a chemical reaction, atoms change the way they are linked together. New products form. But are any atoms lost during the change over? Is any matter destroyed?

The burning of wood and rusting are two examples of chemical reactions.

- Wood burns, and a small amount of ash remains behind.

- A car rusts, and it looks like it's wearing away.

It surely seems that some matter is lost. But is it really? This is how we can find out:

1. Find the mass of the reactants. That means find the mass of <u>all</u> the substances that take part in a chemical reaction.

2. Then find the mass of the products. That means find the mass of <u>all</u> the new substances that form.

If there is a loss of mass, then we know that some matter was destroyed.

If there is no loss of mass, then we know that matter was not destroyed.

In any chemical reaction, there is no mass loss. The mass of the products is the same as the mass of the reactants. In other words, we end up with the same mass as we started with. This means that no matter was destroyed.

In a chemical reaction, matter is not destroyed. This is part of a scientific statement called the **Law of Conservation of Matter**.

Can matter be destroyed? Yes! But not in a chemical reaction. It takes an atomic or nuclear reaction to destroy matter. When matter is destroyed, it changes into energy. This is the idea behind atomic energy.

UNDERSTANDING CONSERVATION OF MATTER

Look at Figures A and B. Then answer the questions.

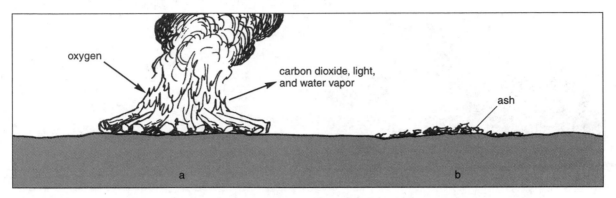

Figure A

Wood, like paper, is made up mostly of carbon and hydrogen.

When wood burns, it links up with oxygen. The reaction produces ash, carbon dioxide, and water vapor. (Heat energy is also produced. But energy has no mass.)

Wood + Oxygen → Ash + Carbon dioxide + Water vapor

1. Name the reactants when wood burns. _____wood   oxygen_____

2. Name the products. _____ash   carbon dioxide   water vapor_____

3. Where does the oxygen come from? _____the air_____

4. The ash remains behind. What happens to the carbon dioxide and water? _____
   _____It blows away._____

5. If the reactants have a mass of 10 kilograms, what will the mass of the products be?
   _____10 kilograms_____

6. Is any matter lost? _____no_____

7. Is matter lost during any chemical reaction? _____no_____

8. In a chemical reaction, the mass of the products equals the mass of the
   _____reactants_____. In other words, "the mass you start with is the mass you
   _____end up with_____."

9. Name the scientific statement that tells us that matter is not destroyed during a
   chemical reaction. _____Law of Conservation of Matter_____

THE RUSTING OF IRON

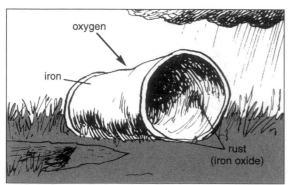

When iron rusts, it links up with oxygen. This is the equation for the reaction:

$$4Fe + 3O_2 \rightarrow 2Fe_2O_3$$

Iron   Oxygen   Iron oxide
(Rust)

Figure B

1. Name the reactants ___iron___ ___oxygen___

2. Where did the oxygen come from? ___the air___

3. What is the chemical name of the product? ___iron oxide___

4. What is the common name of the product? ___rust___

Look at the equation. Answer the questions.

5. How many atoms of iron did we start with? ___4___

6. The atomic mass of iron is 56. What is the mass of all the iron atoms? ___224___

7. How many atoms of oxygen did we start with? ___6___

8. The atomic mass of oxygen is 16. What is the mass of all the oxygen atoms?

   ___96___

9. Altogether, what is the mass of the reactants? ___320___

10. How many atoms of iron did we end with? ___4___

11. What is the mass of all these atoms? ___224___

12. How many atoms of oxygen did we end with? ___6___

13. What is the mass of all these atoms? ___96___

14. Altogether, what is the mass of the product? ___320___

15. Is the mass of the product the same as the mass of the reactants? ___yes___

16. Was any matter lost? ___no___

17. How do you know? ___The mass did not change.___

18. Is any matter destroyed in a chemical reaction? _____no_____

19. What happens to atoms during a chemical reaction? ___They change the way they___ are linked up.

20. The equation for rusting is a "balanced" equation. What do you think this means?
The mass of the reactants equals the mass of the products.

COUNTING ATOMS

Let's work with the equation in a different way. This time let's just count atoms.

$$4Fe + 3O_2 \rightarrow 2Fe_2O_3$$

1. Name the kinds of atoms of the reactant side of the equation. _____iron_____
_____oxygen_____

2. Name the kinds of atoms on the product side. _____iron_____ _____oxygen_____

3. The kinds of atoms on the product side _____are_____ the same as the kinds
of atoms on the reactant side.   are, are not

4. How many atoms of iron are there on the reactant side? _____4_____

5. How many atoms of iron are there on the product side? _____4_____

6. How many atoms of oxygen are there on the reactant side? _____6_____

7. How many atoms of oxygen are there on the product side? _____6_____

8. The number of any kind of atom _____is_____ the same on both sides of the
equation.   is, is not

9. If the number of each kind of atom is the same on both sides of the equation, then
what else is equal? _____the mass of each side_____

10. This shows that matter _____was not_____ destroyed.
        was, was not

CONSERVATION OF MATTER

What You Need to Know (Background Information)

Baking soda has many uses. People use it for cleaning, removing odors, and even brushing their teeth! Its chemical name is sodium bicarbonate. Its formula is $NaHCO_3$.

Vinegar is also very common. People use it in salad dressings and laundry rinses and for many health reasons. Vinegar can relieve burns, insect bites, nausea, and coughs. Its chemical name is acetic acid and its formula is CH_3COOH.

When these two chemicals combine, they produce carbon dioxide (the same gas you exhale when you breathe), water, and sodium acetate. This is the equation for the reaction:

$$NaHCO_3 + CH_3COOH \rightarrow CO_2 + H_2O + NaC_2H_3O_2$$

In this experiment, you will observe what happens during this reaction.

What You Need (Materials)

small plastic container   small sealable plastic bag
vinegar   teaspoon
baking soda   balance scale

What to Do (Procedure)

1. Find the mass of the of the plastic container. Record the mass here.

   <u>Answers will vary.</u>

2. Add about 4 teaspoons of vinegar to the container. Then find the mass of the container + vinegar. Record the mass here. <u>Answers will vary.</u>

3. Subtract the measurement you got in step 1 from the measurement in step 2 to find the mass of just the vinegar. Record the mass here. <u>Answers will vary.</u>

4. Add about 4 teaspoons of baking soda to the small plastic bag and seal it. Find the mass of the bag + baking soda. Record that mass here. <u>Answers will vary.</u>

5. Open the bag and add the vinegar to the baking soda. Quickly seal the bag again. Observe what happens.

6. After the reaction is complete, find the mass of the bag and its contents. Record the mass here.

   <u>Answers will vary.</u>

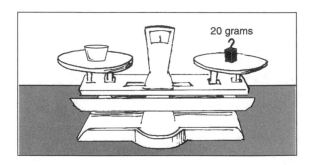

20 grams

Figure C

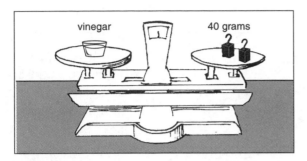

Figure D

1. What was the mass of the vinegar (step 3) + the bag and baking soda (step 4) before the reaction?

   <u>Answers will vary.</u>

2. What was the mass of the bag and its contents after the reaction (step 6)?

   <u>Answers will vary.</u>

3. How did the contents of the bag change in appearance? <u>A gas and white paste were formed.</u>

4. Vinegar mixing with baking soda causes a <u>   chemical   </u> change.

physical, chemical

5. If a chemical reaction destroys matter, then the bag and its contents would become <u>   lighter   </u> .

heavier, lighter

6. Did the bag become lighter after the reaction? <u>   no   </u>

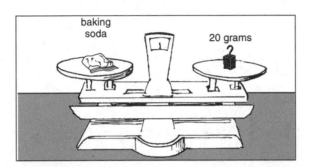

Figure E

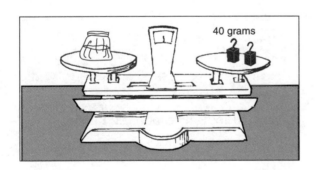

Figure F

Something to Think About (Conclusions)

1. Matter <u> was not </u> destroyed.

was, was not

2. A chemical reaction <u> does not </u> destroy matter.

does, does not

3. If the bag is not closed quickly enough after the vinegar is added, the mass of the bag and its contents might be less after the reaction than before. How could you explain this decrease in mass? <u>Some of the gas might have escaped.</u>

BALANCED OR NOT BALANCED?

Four equations are listed below. Two are balanced, two are not. Figure out which ones are balanced. (Hint: Counting atoms is the easiest way. If the number of each kind of atom is the same on both sides, then the equation is balanced.)

Equations

A. $Zn + H_2SO_4 \rightarrow ZnSO_4 + H_2$

B. $Mg + O_2 \rightarrow 2MgO$

C. $Na_2S + 2HCl \rightarrow 2NaCl + H_2S$

D. $H_2S + SO_2 \rightarrow 3S + 2H_2O$

1. Which equations are balanced? _____A, C_____

2. Which equations are not balanced? _____B, D_____

3. Which equations show the Law of Conservation of Matter? _____A, C_____

4. Which equations do not show the Law of Conservation of Matter? _____B, D_____

REACHING OUT

Figure G *Uranium fuel*

A nuclear reaction destroys matter. Nuclear fuel, like uranium, changes to energy.

How can we show that matter is lost in a nuclear reaction? (Hint: Look back at the vinegar and baking soda experiment.)

Accept all logical responses. Likely

responses include that if the mass of the

products in a nuclear reaction is less

than the mass of the reactants, then

matter was lost.

Lesson **32**

What is a synthesis reaction?

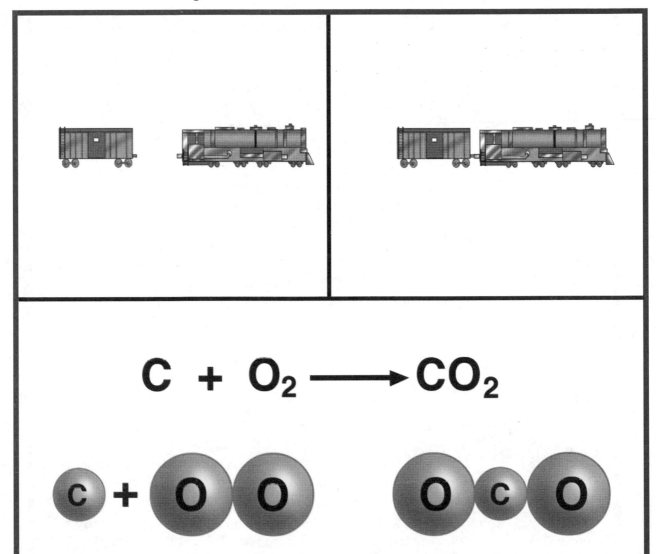

$$C + O_2 \longrightarrow CO_2$$

KEY TERM

synthesis reaction: combining of several substances to form a more complicated substance

LESSON 32 | What is a synthesis reaction?

Chemical reactions are happening around you all the time. A match burns. A car rusts. Food spoils. Leaves decay. These are just a few chemical reactions.

Probably the most important chemical reactions take place in your body. They are happening this very moment. Digestion is a chemical process. So is respiration. In every one of your trillions of cells, chemical reactions are taking place all the time. Life depends upon chemical reactions.

There are several kinds of chemical reactions. One kind is the **synthesis** [SIN-thuh-sis] **reaction.** "Synthesis" means a putting together. A synthesis reaction combines substances, usually elements, to form a compound. When the compound forms, we say it has been synthesized. Below is a "model" of a synthesis reaction.

$$A + B \longrightarrow AB$$

$$\text{Element} + \text{Element} \longrightarrow \text{Compound}$$

Let's study two synthesis reactions.

RUSTING   When iron rusts, it <u>combines</u> with oxygen.

Remember this equation?

$$4Fe + 3O_2 \longrightarrow 2Fe_2O_3$$

$$\text{Iron} + \text{Oxygen} \longrightarrow \text{Iron oxide (rust)}$$

$$\text{Element} + \text{Element} \xrightarrow[\text{to form}]{\text{link up}} \text{Compound}$$

THE BURNING OF CARBON   Charcoal is made of the element carbon (C). When carbon burns, it <u>combines</u> with oxygen. This produces the gas carbon dioxide (CO_2).

$$C + O_2 \longrightarrow CO_2$$

$$\text{Carbon} + \text{Oxygen} \xrightarrow[\text{to form}]{\text{link up}} \text{Carbon dioxide}$$

$$\text{Element} + \text{Element} \longrightarrow \text{Compound}$$

A synthesis reaction is like any other kind of chemical reaction. No matter is created. No matter is destroyed. The atoms just change their arrangement.

UNDERSTANDING SYNTHESIS REACTIONS

Look at Figures A through E and read the explanation. Then answer the questions with each.

When hydrogen explodes, it combines with oxygen. Water is produced. This equation shows what happens:

$$2H_2 \quad + \quad O_2 \quad \longrightarrow 2H_2O$$

Hydrogen + Oxygen ⟶ Water

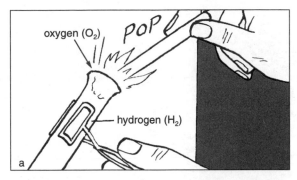

Figure A

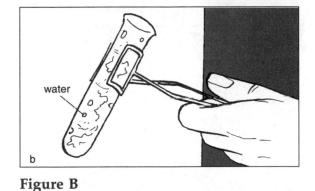

Figure B

1. Hydrogen is ___an element___ .
   <small>an element, a compound</small>

2. Oxygen is ___an element___ .
   <small>an element, a compound</small>

3. Water is ___a compound___ .
   <small>an element, a compound</small>

4. Is the formation of water a synthesis reaction? ___yes___

5. Why is the formation of water a synthesis reaction? ___Hydrogen and oxygen combine to form water.___

When powdered sulfur and iron filings are heated together, they form iron sulfide.

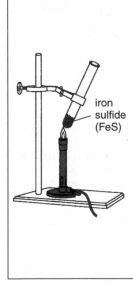

Figure C   **Figure D**

This equation shows what happens:

$$Fe \quad + \quad S \quad \longrightarrow \quad FeS$$

Iron + Sulfur ⟶ Iron sulfide

1. Iron is ___an element___ .
   <small>an element, a compound</small>

2. Sulfur is ___an element___ .
   <small>an element, a compound</small>

3. Iron sulfide is ___a compound___ .
   <small>an element, a compound</small>

4. What happens to the iron and sulfur when they form iron sulfide? ___they combine___

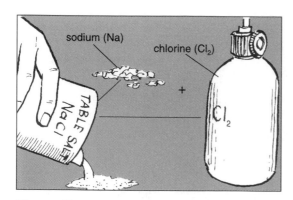

Sodium combines with chlorine to form sodium chloride—common table salt.

This equation shows what happens:

$$2Na \quad + \quad Cl_2 \quad \longrightarrow \quad 2NaCl$$

Sodium + Chlorine ⟶ Sodium chloride

Figure E

1. Sodium is _____an element_____ .
   <u>an element, a compound</u>

2. Chlorine is _____an element_____ .
   <u>an element, a compound</u>

3. Sodium chloride is _____a compound_____ .
   <u>an element, a compound</u>

4. What kind of reaction is the formation of sodium chloride? _____synthesis_____

   Why? _____The sodium and chlorine combine._____

YOUR OWN WORDS

1. What does "synthesis" mean? _____Accept all logical responses._____

2. What does "synthesis reaction" mean? _____Accept all logical responses._____

Two synthesis equations are shown below. They are different from the ones you have already seen.

Equation I $CO_2 + C \quad \longrightarrow \quad 2CO_2$

Equation II $CO_2 + H_2O \quad \longrightarrow \quad H_2CO_3$

3. How is Equation I different from the other synthesis equations in this lesson?

   A compound is combining with an element.

4. How is Equation II different from the other synthesis equations in this lesson?

   Two compounds are combining.

IDENTIFYING SYNTHESIS REACTIONS

Ten equations are listed below. Some are synthesis reactions. Some are not. Make a check (✔) in the correct box next to each equation.

	Equation	A Synthesis Reaction	Not a Synthesis Reaction
1.	$2K + Br_2 \longrightarrow 2KBr$	✔	
2.	$2H_2O \longrightarrow 2H_2 + O_2$		✔
3.	$2NaCl \longrightarrow 2Na + Cl_2$		✔
4.	$4Au + 3O_2 \longrightarrow 2Au_2O_3$	✔	
5.	$2Na + 2HCl \longrightarrow 2NaCl + H_2$		✔
6.	$Cu + Br_2 \longrightarrow CuBr_2$	✔	
7.	$Zn + S \longrightarrow ZnS$	✔	
8.	$2Na + Br_2 \longrightarrow 2NaBr$	✔	
9.	$2HgO \longrightarrow 2Hg + O_2$		✔
10.	$2Na + I_2 \longrightarrow 2NaI$	✔	

TRUE OR FALSE

In the space provided, write "true" if the sentence is true. Write "false" if the sentence is false.

False   **1.** There is only one kind of chemical reaction.

False   **2.** A synthesis reaction separates a compound into its elements.

False   **3.** The reactants of every synthesis reaction are elements.

True   **4.** The product of a synthesis reaction is a compound.

False   **5.** Chemical reactions take place only in the laboratory.

WORD SEARCH

The list on the left contains words that you have used in this Lesson. Find and circle each word where it appears in the box. The spellings may go in any direction: up, down, left, right, or diagonally.

MATTER

POLYVALENT

MASS

REACTANT

FORMULA

PHYSICAL

PRODUCT

YIELDS

CHEMICAL

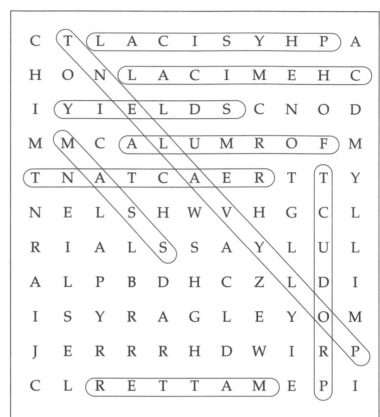

```
C  T  L  A  C  I  S  Y  H  P  A
H  O  N  L  A  C  I  M  E  H  C
I  Y  I  E  L  D  S  C  N  O  D
M  M  C  A  L  U  M  R  O  F  M
T  N  A  T  C  A  E  R  T  T  Y
N  E  L  S  H  W  V  H  G  C  L
R  I  A  L  S  S  A  Y  L  U  L
A  L  P  B  D  H  C  Z  L  D  I
I  S  Y  R  A  G  L  E  Y  O  M
J  E  R  R  R  H  D  W  I  R  P
C  L  R  E  T  T  A  M  E  P  I
```

REACHING OUT

Most compounds made of only two elements have names ending in *-ide*. For example:

$$NaCl = \text{sodium chloride}$$
$$K_2S = \text{potassium sulfide}$$

Can you name these compounds?

	Formula	Name
1.	CaO	calcium oxide
2.	KI	potassium iodide
3.	NaBr	sodium bromide
4.	AgF	silver fluoride
5.	$MgCl_2$	magnesium chloride

What is a decomposition reaction?

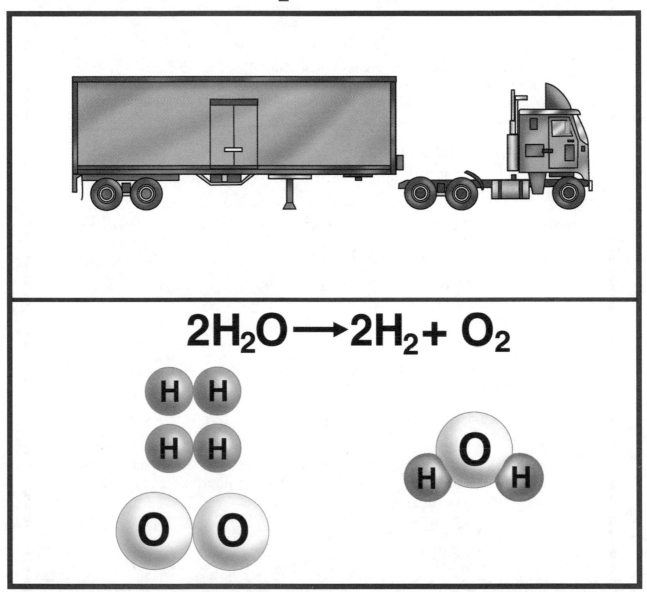

$$2H_2O \longrightarrow 2H_2 + O_2$$

KEY TERMS

decomposition: breakdown of a substance into simpler substances

electrolysis: decomposition of a substance by means of electricity

LESSON 33 | What is a decomposition reaction?

Synthesis reactions build compounds. Anything that can be built can also be taken apart. The breakdown of a compound into simpler substances is called **decomposition** [dee-kahm-puh-ZISH-un]. Decomposition is a chemical process.

Let us look at two examples.

1. Common table salt (sodium chloride) is a compound. It is composed of the elements sodium and chlorine.

Sodium chloride can be melted. If electricity is passed through melted sodium chloride, it decomposes. The molecules unlock. They change back to atoms of sodium and chlorine. This equation shows the reaction:

$$2NaCl \quad \xrightarrow[\text{into}]{\text{breaks down}} \quad 2NA \quad + \quad Cl_2$$

Sodium chloride	Sodium	Chlorine
(compound)	(element)	(element)

The decomposition of a compound by means of electricity is called **electrolysis** [i-lek-TRAHL-uh-sis]. Only certain compounds can be decomposed by electrolysis.

2. Potassium chlorate ($KClO_3$) is a compound. It is composed of the elements potassium, chlorine, and oxygen.

Heat decomposes potassium chlorate. Potassium chlorate changes to oxygen and potassium chloride (a simpler compound). This equation shows the reaction:

$$2KClO_3 \quad \longrightarrow \quad 2KCl \quad + \quad 3O_2$$

Potassium chlorate	Potassium chloride	Oxygen
(compound)	(a simpler compound)	(element)

Notice that the decomposition is not complete. The oxygen has been separated. But the potassium and chlorine are still joined to form the compound potassium chloride. Another kind of decomposition reaction can separate potassium chloride into its elements.

The compounds that can be decomposed this way <u>must</u> be in liquid form.

UNDERSTANDING DECOMPOSITION REACTIONS

Look at Figure A. Then answer the questions or fill in the blanks.

Electrolysis decomposes water. This is the equation for the reaction:

$$2H_2O \longrightarrow 2H_2 + O_2$$

Water   Hydrogen + Oxygen

1. What is the formula for water? ___H_2O___

2. Water is _____a compound_____ .

              an element, a compound

3. Name the elements that make up water.

_____hydrogen   oxygen_____

4. Name the process that decomposes water.

_____electrolysis_____

5. What kind of energy is used?

_____electricity_____

6. When water decomposes, it changes to the

elements ___hydrogen___ and

___oxygen___ .

7. Water is in the ___liquid___ state.

             solid, liquid, gas

8. Hydrogen is in the ___gas___ state.

             solid, liquid, gas

9. Oxygen is in the ___gas___ state.

             solid, liquid, gas

10. Which is simpler, water or the elements that make up water? ___the elements

that make up water___

11. Decomposition ___breaks down___ compounds.

             builds up, breaks down

12. Can electrolysis decompose every compound? ___no___

13. Name another compound that can be decomposed with electrolysis.

_____sodium chloride (NaCl)_____

Figure A

water (H_2O)

oxygen (O_2)

hydrogen (H_2)

6 volt battery

Look at Figure B. Answer the questions.

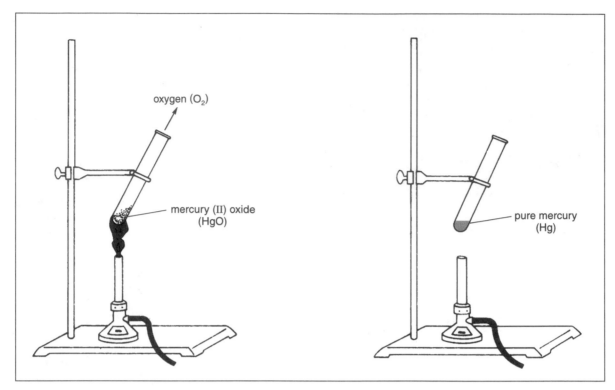

Figure B

Mercury (II) oxide is a solid. Heat decomposes mercury (II) oxide. This is the equation for the reaction.

$$2HgO \quad \xrightarrow{\text{heat}} \quad 2Hg \quad + \quad O_2$$

Mercury (II) oxide $\qquad$ Mercury $\quad + \quad$ Oxygen

1. What is the formula for mercury (II) oxide? _____ HgO _____

2. Mercury (II) oxide is _____ a compound _____ .
   <u>an element, a compound</u>

3. Name the elements that make up mercury (II) oxide. _____ mercury, oxygen _____

4. What happens when mercury (II) oxide is heated? _____ It decomposes. _____

5. What kind of energy decomposes mercury (II) oxide? _____ heat _____

6. When mercury (II) oxide decomposes, it changes to the elements _____ mercury _____

   and _____ oxygen _____ .

7. Mercury (II) oxide is in the _____ solid _____ state.
   <u>solid, liquid, gas</u>

8. Mercury is in the ____liquid____ state.

solid, liquid, gas

9. Oxygen is in the ____gas____ state.

solid, liquid, gas

10. Which is simpler: mercury (II) oxide or the elements that make up mercury (II) oxide? __the elements that make up mercury (II) oxide__

11. The mercury ____stays in the test tube____ .

stays in the test tube, escapes into the air

12. The oxygen ____escapes into the air____ .

stays in the test tube, escapes into the air

13. Can heat decompose every compound? ____no____

14. Name another compound that can be decomposed by heat. __potassium chlorate__

FILL IN THE BLANK

Complete each statement using a term or terms from the list below. Write your answers in the spaces provided.

heating	mercury (II) oxide	electrolysis
potassium chlorate	synthesis	molten sodium chloride
liquid	fewer	decomposition
simpler	water	

1. The combining of substances to form a compound is called ____synthesis____ .

2. The breakdown of a compound into simpler substances is called
   ____decomposition____ .

3. Two methods used to decompose compounds are ____electrolysis____ and
   ____heating____ .

4. For a compound to decompose by electrolysis, it must be in a ____liquid____ state.

5. Two compounds that can be decomposed by electrolysis are
   ____water____ and ____molten sodium chloride____ .

6. Two compounds that can be decomposed by heat are ____mercury (II) oxide____
   and ____potassium chlorate____ .

7. Atoms are ____simpler____ than molecules.

8. KCl is a simpler compound than $KClO_3$ because KCl has ____fewer____
   elements and atoms.

MATCHING

Match each term in Column A with its description in Column B. Write the correct letter in the space provided.

	Column A		Column B
e	1. synthesis reaction	a)	breaks down compounds
a	2. decomposition reaction	b)	uses electricity
c	3. electrolysis and heat	c)	methods of decomposition
b	4. electrolysis	d)	simpler than a compound
d	5. an element	e)	builds compounds

IDENTIFYING DECOMPOSITION REACTIONS

Ten chemical equations are listed below. Some are decomposition reactions. Some are not. Mark a (✔) in the correct box next to each equation.

	Equation	Decomposition Reaction	Not a Decomposition Reaction
1.	$CuCl_2 \rightarrow Cu + Cl_2$	✔	
2.	$3Hf + 2N_2 \rightarrow Hf_3N_4$		✔
3.	$Zn + 2HCl \rightarrow ZnCl_2 + H_2$		✔
4.	$H_2CO_3 \rightarrow H_2O + CO_2$	✔	
5.	$2NaOH \rightarrow 2Na + O_2 + H_2$	✔	
6.	$Fe + S \rightarrow FeS$		✔
7.	$CaCO_3 \rightarrow CaO + CO_2$	✔	
8.	$4P + 5O_2 \rightarrow 2P_2O_5$		✔
9.	$C + O_2 \rightarrow CO_2$		✔
10.	$Ca(OH)_2 \rightarrow CaO + H_2O$	✔	

REACHING OUT

1. Does boiling decompose water? __no__

2. What does boiling do to water? __It changes water into steam. It changes the__ state of water.

Lesson

34

What is a replacement reaction?

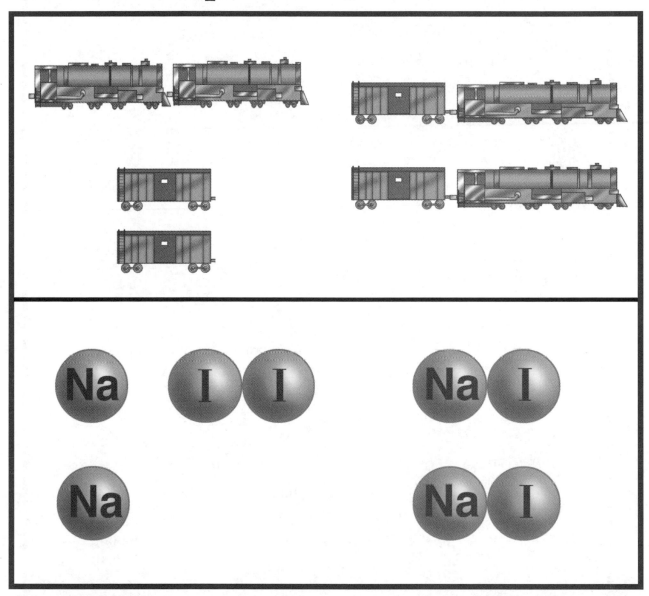

215

LESSON 34 | What is a replacement reaction?

Imagine that three children are playing.

Two are holding hands. The other is alone.

The child that was alone now joins the others. He takes the place of one of the children.

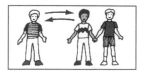

Now a different child is alone.

We have the same children that we started with. But, now they are arranged in a different way.

Some chemical reactions work like this. A free element takes the place of or replaces another element of a compound.

The element that was replaced is now "free."

$$A \quad + \quad BC \quad \longrightarrow \quad AC \quad + \quad B$$
free element   compound   new compound   new free element

Let's study an actual **replacement reaction**—one between zinc (Zn) and hydrochloric acid (HCl).

The zinc is the "free" element. The hydrochloric acid is in the compound.

$$Zn \quad + \quad 2HCl \quad \longrightarrow \quad ZnCl_2 \quad + \quad H_2$$
The zinc replaces the hydrogen.   The hydrogen is set free.

The reaction produces a new compound, zinc chloride ($ZnCl_2$), and free hydrogen (H_2). Notice that the elements we started with are the elements we ended with. They are just arranged in a different way.

This kind of reaction is called a single **replacement reaction**. In a single replacement reaction, a free element replaces a different element of a compound.

UNDERSTANDING SINGLE REPLACEMENT REACTIONS

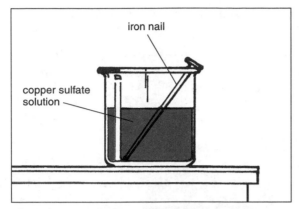

Figure A

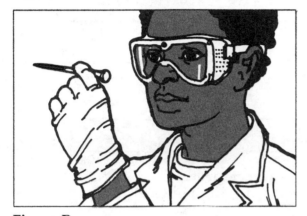

Figure B

What You Need (Materials)

iron nail
copper sulfate solution
beaker

How to Do the Experiment (Procedure)

Place an iron nail in copper sulfate solution.

Remove the nail in a few minutes.

What You Saw (Observations)

The nail is coated with copper.

This is the equation for the reaction.

$$Fe + CuSO_4 \rightarrow FeSO_4 + Cu$$

Iron   Copper sulfate   Iron sulfate   Copper

1. Name the free element we started with. _____iron_____

2. Name the compound we started with. _____copper sulfate_____

3. Name the free element we ended with. _____copper_____

4. Name the compound we ended with. _____iron sulfate_____

5. a) Which element did the iron replace? _____copper_____

   b) What happened to this element? _____It was set free._____

6. What do we call this kind of chemical reaction? _____single replacement_____

7. What happens during a single replacement reaction? _____A free element_____ takes the place of or replaces another element.

IDENTIFYING SINGLE REPLACEMENT REACTIONS

Six equations are listed below. Some are single replacement reactions. Some are not. Mark a check (✔) in the correct box next to each equation.

	Equation	Single replacement reaction	Not a single replacement reaction
1.	$C + 2S \rightarrow CS_2$		✔
2.	$H_2O_2 \rightarrow H_2 + O_2$		✔
3.	$2Al + 6HCl \rightarrow 2AlCl_3 + 3H_2$	✔	
4.	$2K + Cl_2 \rightarrow 2KCl$		✔
5.	$Zn + PbO \rightarrow ZnO + Pb$	✔	
6.	$Fe + CuSO_4 \rightarrow FeSO_4 + Cu$	✔	

DOUBLE REPLACEMENT REACTIONS

A <u>single</u> replacement reaction takes place between an element and a compound. The free element replaces one of the elements of the compound. This produces a new compound and a new free element.

$$\underset{\text{free element}}{A} \quad + \quad \underset{\text{compound}}{BC} \quad \longrightarrow \quad \underset{\text{new compound}}{AC} \quad + \quad \underset{\text{new free element}}{B}$$

A <u>double</u> replacement reaction takes place between <u>two</u> compounds. A part of one compound changes place with a part of the other compound.

Let us use playing children as models again to see what happens.

Children A and B stand for compound AB.
Children C and D stand for compound CD.

Figure C

Child A changes place with child C.

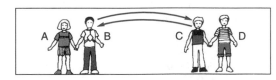

Figure D

What do we have now? Instead of compounds AB and CD, we have two new compounds— CB and AD.

When there are two change overs, a double replacement has taken place.

Figure E

Now let us study an actual double replacement reaction—the reaction between sodium hydroxide (NaOH), and hydrochloric acid (HCl).

$$NaOH + HCl \longrightarrow NaCl + H_2O, \text{ water}$$

- The sodium and hydrogen change places.

- Two new compounds form—NaCl (common table salt) and H_2O (water).

Now you try. Read each equation carefully. Then answer the questions or fill in the blanks with each.

Equation I $BaCl_2$ + Na_2SO_4 → $BaSO_4$ + $2NaCl$
                Barium chloride   Sodium sulfate   Barium sulfate   Sodium chloride

1. Name the reactants. _____ barium chloride _____   _____ sodium sulfate _____

2. The reactants are _____ both compounds _____ .
                    both elements, both compounds, an element and a compound

3. The barium changed places with the _____ sodium _____ .
                                        sulfate, chlorine, sodium

4. Name the products. _____ barium sulfate _____   _____ sodium chloride _____

5. The products are _____ both compounds _____ .
                    both elements, both compounds, an element and a compound

6. What kind of chemical reaction is this? _____ double replacement _____

7. Double replacement is the reaction of two _____ compounds _____ to form two new
   _____ compounds _____ .

Equation II $AgNO_3$ + $NaBr$ → $AgBr$ + $NaNO_3$
                Silver nitrate   Sodium bromide   Silver bromide   Sodium nitrate

8. Name the reactants. _____ silver nitrate _____   _____ sodium bromide _____

9. The reactants are _____ both compounds _____ .
                    both elements, both compounds, an element and a compound

10. The silver changed places with the _____ sodium _____ .
                                        sulfate, chlorine, sodium

11. Name the products. _____ silver bromide _____   _____ sodium nitrate _____

12. The products are _____ both compounds _____ .
                    both elements, both compounds, an element and a compound

13. What kind of chemical reaction is this? _____ double replacement _____

IDENTIFYING DOUBLE REPLACEMENT REACTIONS

Eight equations are listed below. Some are double replacement reactions. Some are not. Mark a check (✔) in the correct box next to each equation.

	Equation	Double replacement reaction	Not a double replacement reaction
1.	$Mg(OH)_2 + 2HCl \rightarrow MgCl_2 + 2HOH$	✔	
2.	$C_6H_{10}O_5 + H_2O \rightarrow C_6H_{12}O_6$		✔
3.	$Na_2SO_4 + BaCl_2 \rightarrow 2NaCl + BaSO_4$	✔	
4.	$3Mg + N_2 \rightarrow Mg_3N_2$		✔
5.	$H_2SO_4 + BaCl_2 \rightarrow 2HCl + BaSO_4$	✔	
6.	$ZnCO_3 \rightarrow ZnO + CO_2$		✔
7.	$CuSO_4 + H_2S \rightarrow H_2SO_4 + CuS$	✔	
8.	$NH_4NO_3 \rightarrow 2H_2O + N_2O$		✔

IDENTIFYING CHEMICAL REACTIONS

Ten chemical equations are listed below. Identify each kind of reaction: synthesis, decomposition, single replacement, or double replacement.

	Equation	Kind of reaction
1.	$N_2 + 3H_2 \rightarrow 2NH_3$	synthesis
2.	$2Br_2 + 2H_2O \rightarrow 4HBr + O_2$	single replacement
3.	$Mg + 2HCl \rightarrow MgCl_2 + H_2$	single replacement
4.	$2KBr + H_2SO_4 \rightarrow K_2SO_4 + 2HBr$	double replacement
5.	$H_2SO_3 \rightarrow H_2O + SO_2$	decomposition
6.	$Na_2S + 2HCl \rightarrow 2NaCl + H_2S$	double replacement
7.	$2Na + I_2 \rightarrow 2NaI$	synthesis
8.	$NaCl + AgNO_3 \rightarrow NaNO_3 + AgCl$	double replacement
9.	$H_2 + Cl_2 \rightarrow 2HCl$	synthesis
10.	$H_2CO_3 \rightarrow H_2O + CO_2$	decomposition

What are oxidation and reduction?

KEY TERMS

oxidation: linkup of oxygen with another substance; a loss of electrons

reduction: separation of oxygen from a substance; a gain of electrons

LESSON 35 | What are oxidation and reduction?

Oxidation and reduction are opposite kinds of chemical reactions.

Oxidation [ahk-suh-DAY-shun] takes place when oxygen combines with another substance.

For example, when a flashbulb goes off, oxygen combines with aluminum.

The aluminum becomes oxidized. Aluminum oxide (Al_2O_3) forms.

$$4Al \quad + \quad 3O_2 \quad \longrightarrow \quad 2Al_2O_3$$

Aluminum   Oxygen   Aluminum oxide

Reduction [ri-DUK-shun] takes place when oxygen separates from a compound.

For example, electrolysis decomposes molten aluminum oxide (Al_2O_3). The oxygen separates from the aluminum. We say the aluminum oxide is reduced.

$$2Al_2O_3 \quad \longrightarrow \quad 4Al \quad + \quad 3O_2$$

Aluminum oxide   Aluminum   Oxygen

Here is another reduction equation. Notice what happens to the oxygen.

$$2Fe_2O_3 \quad + \quad 3C \quad \longrightarrow \quad 3CO_2 \quad + \quad 4Fe$$

Iron oxide   Carbon   Carbon dioxide   Iron

The oxygen has separated from the iron. But the oxygen is not free oxygen. It is now part of the compound carbon dioxide. It makes no difference whether a separated oxygen becomes free oxygen or part of a new compound. As long as oxygen is separated from a compound, the reaction is reduction.

SLOW AND RAPID OXIDATION

Figure A *Rusting is an example of slow oxidation.*

Figure B *Fire is an example of rapid oxidation.*

UNDERSTANDING OXIDATION AND REDUCTION

Look at Figures C and D. Study the equations. Then answer the questions or fill in the blanks.

The Burning of Carbon

This equation describes what happens when carbon burns:

$$C + O_2 \longrightarrow CO_2$$

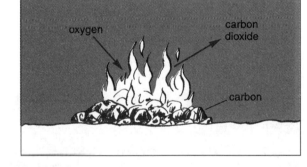

Figure C

1. Name the elements that react together when carbon burns.

   _____carbon_____   _____oxygen_____

2. **a)** When carbon burns, oxygen ___combines with___ the carbon.
   <small>combines with, separates from</small>

   b) What product forms? ___carbon dioxide___

3. In oxidation, oxygen ___combines with___ another substance.
   <small>combines with, separates from</small>

4. In reduction, oxygen ___separates from___ a compound.
   <small>combines with, separates from</small>

5. When carbon burns, the carbon is ___oxidized___ .
   <small>oxidized, reduced</small>

The Electrolysis of Water

The equation for the electrolysis of water is:

$$2H_2O \longrightarrow 2H_2 + O_2$$

6. Name the elements that make up water.

   ___hydrogen___   ___oxygen___

7. Electrolysis ___decomposes___ water.
   forms, decomposes

8. When water decomposes, oxygen

   ___separates from___ hydrogen.
   combines with, separates from

9. The separation of oxygen from a com-

   pound is called ___reduction___.
   oxidation, reduction

10. In the electrolysis of water, the hydrogen is

   ___reduced___.
   oxidized, reduced

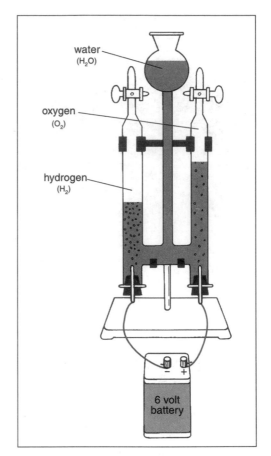

Figure D

ANOTHER VIEW OF OXIDATION AND REDUCTION

Oxidation combines oxygen with another substance.

Reduction separates oxygen from a compound.

This is true. But to a chemist, oxidation and reduction mean even more. A chemist thinks of oxidation and reduction in terms of <u>electrons lost</u> or <u>electrons gained</u>.

To a chemist,

• Oxidation means a loss of electrons.

• Reduction means a gain of electrons.

The reaction may or may not involve oxygen. This means that oxidation and reduction can happen without oxygen. All that is needed is a loss of electrons by one atom and the gain of electrons by some other atom.

Oxidation and reduction always happen together. It is easy to understand why . . . When one atom loses electrons, some other atom gains them.

Let us look at the burning of carbon and the electrolysis of water again. This time, look in terms of electrons gained and electrons lost.

Look at Figure E. Answer the questions or fill in the blanks.

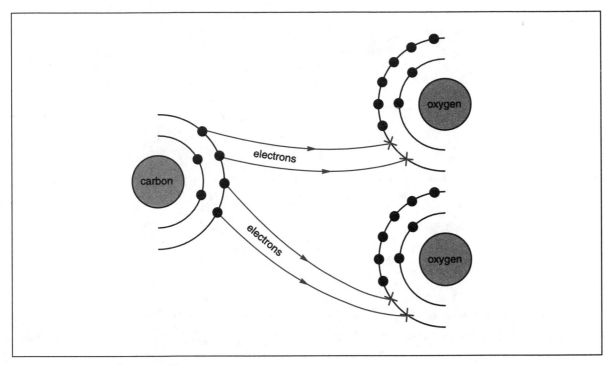

Figure E   *What happens when carbon burns*

1. When carbon burns, the carbon _____lends_____ electrons and the oxygen
    lends, borrows

    _____borrows_____ electrons.
    lends, borrows

2. When carbon burns, the carbon _____loses_____ electrons and oxygen
    gains, loses

    _____gains_____ electrons.
    gains, loses

3. Oxidation is the _____loss_____ of electrons.
    gain, loss

4. Reduction is the _____gain_____ of electrons.
    gain, loss

5. When carbon burns, the carbon is _____oxidized_____ and the oxygen is
    oxidized, reduced

    _____reduced_____ .
    oxidized, reduced

6. Oxidation and reduction happen together because electrons _____lost_____ by

    one atom are _____gained_____ by some other atom.

THE ELECTROLYSIS OF WATER

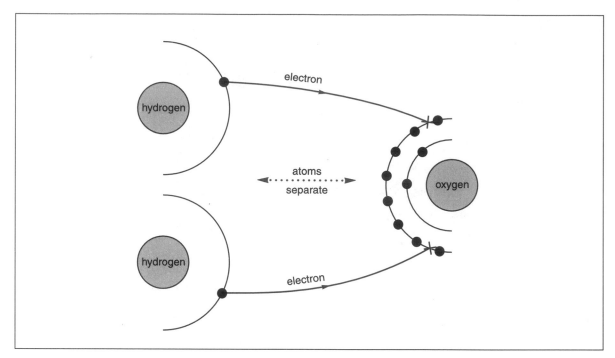

Figure F *What happens during the electrolysis of water*

7. Electrolysis ___decomposes___ water.
   _{forms, decomposes}

8. When water decomposes, electrons move from the ___hydrogen___ to the
   _{hydrogen, oxygen}

   ___oxygen___ .
   _{hydrogen, oxygen}

9. The hydrogen ___gains___ electrons and the oxygen ___loses___
   _{gains, loses}   _{gains, loses}

   electrons.

10. Oxidation is the ___loss___ of electrons.
    _{gain, loss}

11. Reduction is the ___gain___ of electrons.
    _{gain, loss}

12. During the electrolysis of water, the hydrogen is ___reduced___ and the
    _{oxidized, reduced}

    oxygen is ___oxidized___ .
    _{oxidized, reduced}

13. Why do oxidation and reduction always happen together? _____

    ___Electrons lost by one atom are gained by another atom.___

OXIDATION OR REDUCTION

Each equation listed below is either an oxidation or a reduction reaction. Which one is it? Put a check (✔) in the correct box next to each equation. Remember to look in the direction of the arrow only (not the reverse).

	Equation	Oxidation	Reduction
1.	$2Ba + O_2 \rightarrow 2BaO$	✔	
2.	$2HgO \rightarrow 2Hg + O_2$		✔
3.	$ZnO + C \rightarrow Zn + CO$		✔
4.	$4Na + O_2 \rightarrow 2Na_2O$	✔	
5.	$CuO + H_2 \rightarrow Cu + H_2O$		✔
6.	$N_2 + O_2 \rightarrow 2NO$	✔	
7.	$4Ag + O_2 \rightarrow 2Ag_2O$	✔	
8.	$SnO_2 + 2C \rightarrow Sn + 2CO$		✔
9.	$C + O_2 \rightarrow CO_2$	✔	
10.	$Fe_2O_3 + 3CO \rightarrow 2Fe + 3CO_2$		✔

REACHING OUT

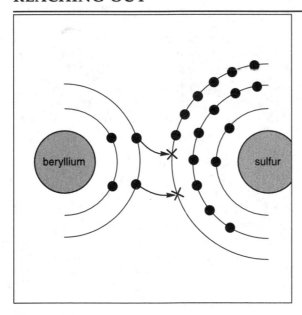

Figure G

Beryllium links up with sulfur to form beryllium sulfide.

$$Be + S \quad \xrightarrow{\hspace{1cm}} \quad BeS$$

No oxygen is involved in this reaction. Yet it is an oxidation-reduction reaction.

Why is this an oxidation-reduction reaction? <u>Because the beryllium loses</u>

<u>electrons and the sulfur gains electrons.</u>

SCIENCE *EXTRA*

Pharmacist

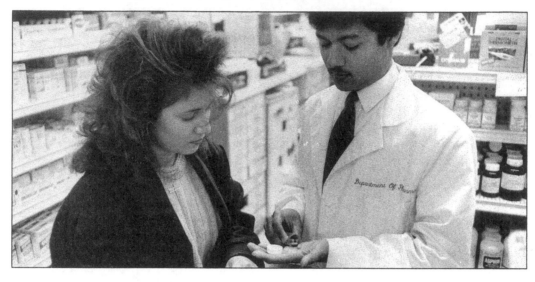

Have you ever taken a prescription drug to get better when you were sick? If you have, then you have two people to thank.

The first person is obvious — your doctor. The doctor examined you, figured out what was wrong with you, and wrote up a prescription. The second person is not as obvious but is just as important. It is your pharmacist.

A pharmacist is a person who prepares prescriptions. Pharmacists understand the chemical compositions of medicines. Therefore, they can safely mix them. Pharmacists know what medicines are safe to take together and what medicines could be harmful if used together. Pharmacists also may know what a person's allergies are and if they would have an allergic reaction to certain medications.

Pharmacists, like doctors, know a great deal about medicine and how to help people get well. Therefore, pharmacists can help you choose non-prescription medicines. Non-prescription medicines are also called over-the-counter medicines. If you tell your pharmacist about a medical problem you are having, he or she may be able to recommend an over-the-counter remedy or suggest that you see your doctor.

Pharmacists can work in a pharmacy, drugstore, or a hospital filling prescriptions. Pharmacists can also work for a company that develops medications. They work in laboratories and try to develop new and improved drugs.

As you can see, being a pharmacist is both interesting and rewarding. To become a pharmacist, you should study chemistry, biology, and math in school. Pharmacists usually study for five years at a College of Pharmacy. After they graduate, students work in an internship with a pharmacist. Finally, students take a state exam to receive a license to become a pharmacist.

THE METRIC SYSTEM

METRIC-ENGLISH CONVERSIONS

	Metric to English	English to Metric
Length	1 kilometer = 0.621 mile (mi)	1 mi = 1.61 km
	1 meter = 3.28 feet (ft)	1 ft = 0.305 m
	1 centimeter = 0.394 inch (in)	1 in = 2.54 cm
Area	1 square meter = 10.763 square feet	$1\ ft^2 = 0.0929\ m^2$
	1 square centimeter = 0.155 square inch	$1\ in^2 = 6.452\ cm^2$
Volume	1 cubic meter = 35.315 cubic feet	$1\ ft^3 = 0.0283\ m^3$
	1 cubic centimeter = 0.0610 cubic inches	$1\ in^3 = 16.39\ cm^3$
	1 liter = .2642 gallon (gal)	1 gal = 3.79 L
	1 liter = 1.06 quart (qt)	1 qt = 0.94 L
Mass	1 kilogram = 2.205 pound (lb)	1 lb = 0.4536 kg
	1 gram = 0.0353 ounce (oz)	1 oz = 28.35 g
Temperature	Celsius = 5/9 (°F –32)	Fahrenheit = 9/5°C + 32
	0°C = 32°F (Freezing point of water)	72°F = 22°C (Room temperature)
	100°C = 212°F	98.6°F = 37°C
	(Boiling point of water)	(Human body temperature)

METRIC UNITS

The basic unit is printed in capital letters.

Length	Symbol
Kilometer	km
METER	m
centimeter	cm
millimeter	mm

Area	Symbol
square kilometer	km^2
SQUARE METER	m^2
square millimeter	mm^2

Volume	Symbol
CUBIC METER	m^3
cubic millimeter	mm^3
liter	L
milliliter	mL

Mass	Symbol
KILOGRAM	kg
gram	g

Temperature	Symbol
degree Celsius	°C

SOME COMMON METRIC PREFIXES

Prefix		Meaning
micro-	=	0.000001, or 1/1,000,000
milli-	=	0.001, or 1/1,000
centi-	=	0.01, or 1/100
deci-	=	0.1, or 1/10
deka-	=	10
hecto-	=	100
kilo-	=	1,000
mega-	=	1,000,000

SOME METRIC RELATIONSHIPS

Unit	Relationship
kilometer	1 km = 1,000 m
meter	1 m = 100 cm
centimeter	1 cm = 10 mm
millimeter	1 mm = 0.1 cm
liter	1 L = 1,000 mL
milliliter	1 mL = 0.001 L
tonne	1 t = 1,000 kg
kilogram	1 kg = 1,000 g
gram	1 g = 1,000 mg
centigram	1 cg = 10 mg
milligram	1 mg = 0.001 g

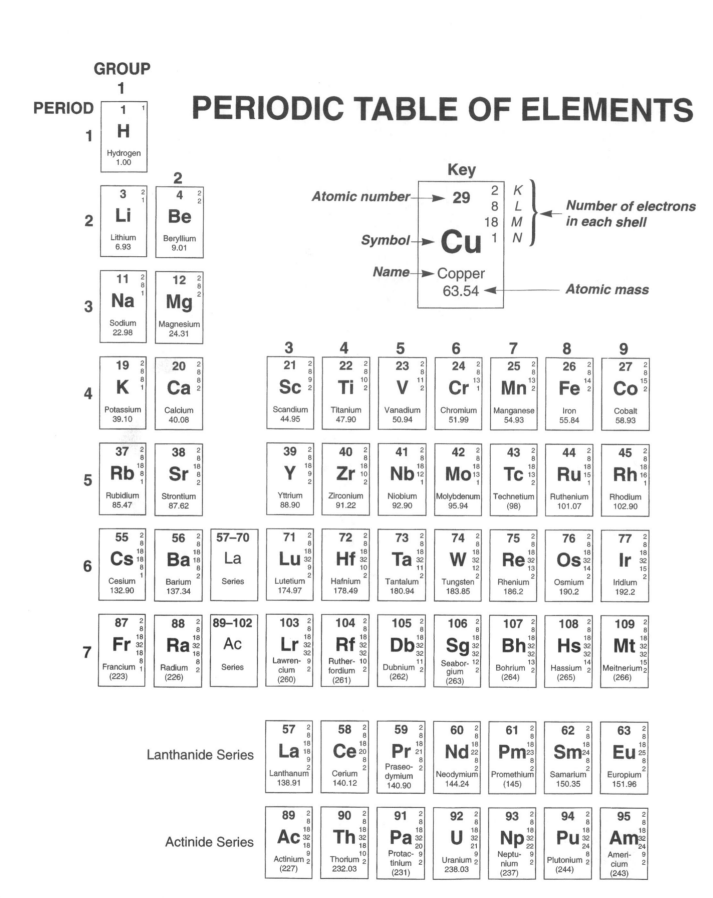

PERIODIC TABLE OF ELEMENTS

Key

Atomic number → 29 — K: 2, L: 8, M: 18, N: 1 (Number of electrons in each shell)

Symbol → **Cu**

Name → Copper

Atomic mass → 63.54

GROUP 1	2		3	4	5	6	7	8	9

PERIOD 1

1 — **H** — Hydrogen 1.00 (K: 1)

PERIOD 2

3 — **Li** — Lithium 6.93 (2, 1)
4 — **Be** — Beryllium 9.01 (2, 2)

PERIOD 3

11 — **Na** — Sodium 22.98 (2, 8, 1)
12 — **Mg** — Magnesium 24.31 (2, 8, 2)

PERIOD 4

19 — **K** — Potassium 39.10 (2, 8, 8, 1)
20 — **Ca** — Calcium 40.08 (2, 8, 8, 2)
21 — **Sc** — Scandium 44.95 (2, 8, 9, 2)
22 — **Ti** — Titanium 47.90 (2, 8, 10, 2)
23 — **V** — Vanadium 50.94 (2, 8, 11, 2)
24 — **Cr** — Chromium 51.99 (2, 8, 13, 1)
25 — **Mn** — Manganese 54.93 (2, 8, 13, 2)
26 — **Fe** — Iron 55.84 (2, 8, 14, 2)
27 — **Co** — Cobalt 58.93 (2, 8, 15, 2)

PERIOD 5

37 — **Rb** — Rubidium 85.47 (2, 8, 18, 8, 1)
38 — **Sr** — Strontium 87.62 (2, 8, 18, 8, 2)
39 — **Y** — Yttrium 88.90 (2, 8, 18, 9, 2)
40 — **Zr** — Zirconium 91.22 (2, 8, 18, 10, 2)
41 — **Nb** — Niobium 92.90 (2, 8, 18, 12, 1)
42 — **Mo** — Molybdenum 95.94 (2, 8, 18, 13, 1)
43 — **Tc** — Technetium (98) (2, 8, 18, 13, 2)
44 — **Ru** — Ruthenium 101.07 (2, 8, 18, 15, 1)
45 — **Rh** — Rhodium 102.90 (2, 8, 18, 16, 1)

PERIOD 6

55 — **Cs** — Cesium 132.90 (2, 8, 18, 18, 8, 1)
56 — **Ba** — Barium 137.34 (2, 8, 18, 18, 8, 2)
57–70 — **La** Series
71 — **Lu** — Lutetium 174.97 (2, 8, 18, 32, 9, 2)
72 — **Hf** — Hafnium 178.49 (2, 8, 18, 32, 10, 2)
73 — **Ta** — Tantalum 180.94 (2, 8, 18, 32, 11, 2)
74 — **W** — Tungsten 183.85 (2, 8, 18, 32, 12, 2)
75 — **Re** — Rhenium 186.2 (2, 8, 18, 32, 13, 2)
76 — **Os** — Osmium 190.2 (2, 8, 18, 32, 14, 2)
77 — **Ir** — Iridium 192.2 (2, 8, 18, 32, 15, 2)

PERIOD 7

87 — **Fr** — Francium (223) (2, 8, 18, 32, 18, 8, 1)
88 — **Ra** — Radium (226) (2, 8, 18, 32, 18, 8, 2)
89–102 — **Ac** Series
103 — **Lr** — Lawrencium (260) (2, 8, 18, 32, 32, 9, 2)
104 — **Rf** — Rutherfordium (261) (2, 8, 18, 32, 32, 10, 2)
105 — **Db** — Dubnium (262) (2, 8, 18, 32, 32, 11, 2)
106 — **Sg** — Seaborgium (263) (2, 8, 18, 32, 32, 12, 2)
107 — **Bh** — Bohrium (264) (2, 8, 18, 32, 32, 13, 2)
108 — **Hs** — Hassium (265) (2, 8, 18, 32, 32, 14, 2)
109 — **Mt** — Meitnerium (266) (2, 8, 18, 32, 32, 15, 2)

Lanthanide Series

57 — **La** — Lanthanum 138.91 (2, 8, 18, 18, 9, 2)
58 — **Ce** — Cerium 140.12 (2, 8, 18, 20, 8, 2)
59 — **Pr** — Praseodymium 140.90 (2, 8, 18, 21, 8, 2)
60 — **Nd** — Neodymium 144.24 (2, 8, 18, 22, 8, 2)
61 — **Pm** — Promethium (145) (2, 8, 18, 23, 8, 2)
62 — **Sm** — Samarium 150.35 (2, 8, 18, 24, 8, 2)
63 — **Eu** — Europium 151.96 (2, 8, 18, 25, 8, 2)

Actinide Series

89 — **Ac** — Actinium (227) (2, 8, 18, 32, 18, 9, 2)
90 — **Th** — Thorium 232.03 (2, 8, 18, 32, 18, 10, 2)
91 — **Pa** — Protactinium (231) (2, 8, 18, 32, 20, 9, 2)
92 — **U** — Uranium 238.03 (2, 8, 18, 32, 21, 9, 2)
93 — **Np** — Neptunium (237) (2, 8, 18, 32, 22, 9, 2)
94 — **Pu** — Plutonium (244) (2, 8, 18, 32, 24, 8, 2)
95 — **Am** — Americium (243) (2, 8, 18, 32, 24, 9, 2)

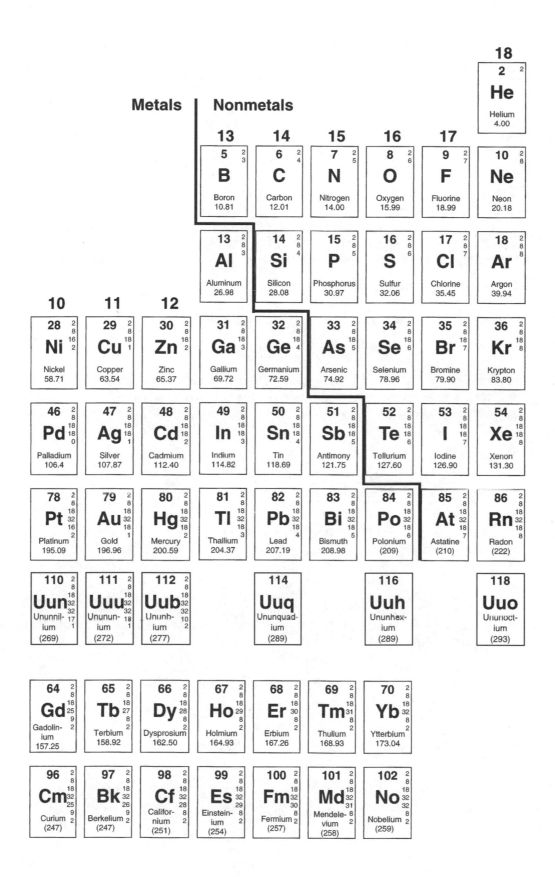

Metals | Nonmetals

18
2 ²
He
Helium
4.00

13	14	15	16	17
5 ²₃	**6** ²₄	**7** ²₅	**8** ²₆	**9** ²₇
B	**C**	**N**	**O**	**F**
Boron	Carbon	Nitrogen	Oxygen	Fluorine
10.81	12.01	14.00	15.99	18.99

10 ²₈
Ne
Neon
20.18

13 ²₈₃	**14** ²₈₄	**15** ²₈₅	**16** ²₈₆	**17** ²₈₇	**18** ²₈₈
Al	**Si**	**P**	**S**	**Cl**	**Ar**
Aluminum	Silicon	Phosphorus	Sulfur	Chlorine	Argon
26.98	28.08	30.97	32.06	35.45	39.94

10	11	12

28 ²₈¹⁶₂	**29** ²₈¹⁸₁	**30** ²₈¹⁸₂	**31** ²₈¹⁸₃	**32** ²₈¹⁸₄	**33** ²₈¹⁸₅	**34** ²₈¹⁸₆	**35** ²₈¹⁸₇	**36** ²₈¹⁸₈
Ni	**Cu**	**Zn**	**Ga**	**Ge**	**As**	**Se**	**Br**	**Kr**
Nickel	Copper	Zinc	Gallium	Germanium	Arsenic	Selenium	Bromine	Krypton
58.71	63.54	65.37	69.72	72.59	74.92	78.96	79.90	83.80

46 ²₈¹⁸¹⁸₀	**47** ²₈¹⁸¹⁸₁	**48** ²₈¹⁸¹⁸₂	**49** ²₈¹⁸¹⁸₃	**50** ²₈¹⁸¹⁸₄	**51** ²₈¹⁸¹⁸₅	**52** ²₈¹⁸¹⁸₆	**53** ²₈¹⁸¹⁸₇	**54** ²₈¹⁸¹⁸₈
Pd	**Ag**	**Cd**	**In**	**Sn**	**Sb**	**Te**	**I**	**Xe**
Palladium	Silver	Cadmium	Indium	Tin	Antimony	Tellurium	Iodine	Xenon
106.4	107.87	112.40	114.82	118.69	121.75	127.60	126.90	131.30

78 ²₈¹⁸³²¹⁶₂	**79** ²₈¹⁸³²¹⁸₁	**80** ²₈¹⁸³²¹⁸₂	**81** ²₈¹⁸³²¹⁸₃	**82** ²₈¹⁸³²¹⁸₄	**83** ²₈¹⁸³²¹⁸₅	**84** ²₈¹⁸³²¹⁸₆	**85** ²₈¹⁸³²¹⁸₇	**86** ²₈¹⁸³²¹⁸₈
Pt	**Au**	**Hg**	**Tl**	**Pb**	**Bi**	**Po**	**At**	**Rn**
Platinum	Gold	Mercury	Thallium	Lead	Bismuth	Polonium	Astatine	Radon
195.09	196.96	200.59	204.37	207.19	208.98	(209)	(210)	(222)

110 ²₈¹⁸³²₁₇	**111** ²₈¹⁸³²₁	**112** ²₈¹⁸³²₁₀		**114**		**116**		**118**
Uun	**Uuu**	**Uub**		**Uuq**		**Uuh**		**Uuo**
Ununnil-	Ununun-	Ununb-		Ununquad-		Ununhex-		Ununoct-
ium	ium	ium		ium		ium		ium
(269)	(272)	(277)		(289)		(289)		(293)

64 ²₈¹⁸²⁵₉₂	**65** ²₈¹⁸²⁷₈₂	**66** ²₈¹⁸²⁸₈₂	**67** ²₈¹⁸²⁹₈₂	**68** ²₈¹⁸³⁰₈₂	**69** ²₈¹⁸³¹₈₂	**70** ²₈¹⁸³²₈₂
Gd	**Tb**	**Dy**	**Ho**	**Er**	**Tm**	**Yb**
Gadolin-	Terbium	Dysprosium	Holmium	Erbium	Thulium	Ytterbium
ium	158.92	162.50	164.93	167.26	168.93	173.04
157.25						

96 ²₈¹⁸³²²⁵₉₂	**97** ²₈¹⁸³²²⁶₉₂	**98** ²₈¹⁸³²²⁸₈₂	**99** ²₈¹⁸³²²⁹₈₂	**100** ²₈¹⁸³²³⁰₈₂	**101** ²₈¹⁸³²³¹₈₂	**102** ²₈¹⁸³²³²₈₂
Cm	**Bk**	**Cf**	**Es**	**Fm**	**Md**	**No**
Curium	Berkelium	Califor-	Einstein-	Fermium	Mendele-	Nobelium
(247)	(247)	nium	ium	(257)	vium	(259)
		(251)	(254)		(258)	

SAFETY ALERT SYMBOLS

 CLOTHING PROTECTION • A lab coat protects clothing from stains. • Always confine loose clothing.

 EYE SAFETY • Always wear safety goggles. • If anything gets in your eyes, flush them with plenty of water. • Be sure you know how to use the emergency wash system in the laboratory.

 FIRE SAFETY • Never get closer to an open flame than is necessary. • Never reach across an open flame. • Confine loose clothing. • Tie back loose hair. • Know the location of the fire extinguisher and fire blanket. • Turn off gas valves when not in use. • Use proper procedures when lighting any burner.

 POISON • Never touch, taste, or smell any unknown substance. Wait for your teacher's instruction.

 CAUSTIC SUBSTANCES • Some chemicals can irritate and burn the skin. If a chemical spills on your skin, flush it with plenty of water. Notify your teacher without delay.

 HEATING SAFETY • Handle hot objects with tongs or insulated gloves. • Put hot objects on a special lab surface or on a heat-resistant pad, never directly on a desk or table top.

 SHARP OBJECTS • Handle sharp objects carefully. • Never point a sharp object at yourself, or anyone else. • Cut in the direction away from your body.

 TOXIC VAPORS • Some vapors (gases) can injure the skin, eyes, and lungs. Never inhale vapors directly. • Use your hand to "wave" a small amount of vapor toward your nose.

 GLASSWARE SAFETY • Never use broken or chipped glassware. • Never pick up broken glass with your bare hands.

 CLEAN UP • Wash your hands thoroughly after any laboratory activity.

 ELECTRICAL SAFETY • Never use an electrical appliance near water or on a wet surface. • Do not use wires if the wire covering seems worn. • Never handle electrical equipment with wet hands.

 DISPOSAL • Discard all materials properly according to your teacher's directions.

GLOSSARY/INDEX

absorb: to take in, 28

acid: substance that reacts with metals to release hydrogen, 144

base: substance formed when metals react with water, 150

borrow: to use something that belongs to someone or something else, 58

calorie [KAL-uh-ree]:   unit used to measure heat, 34

Celsius [SEL-see-us]:   metric temperature scale, 40

chemical change: change in matter that produces new substances, 66, 190

chemical equation: set of symbols and formulas that describe a chemical change, 190

chemical formula: short way of writing a compound, 52

chemical reaction: process involving a chemical change, 66

coagulation [koh-ag-yoo-LAY-shun]:   use of chemicals to make the particles in a suspension clump together, 98

coefficient [koh-uh-FISH-unt]:   number that shows how many molecules of a substance are involved in a chemical reaction, 187

colloid [KAHL-oyd]:   suspension in which the particles are permanently suspended, 90, 95

compound: matter made up of two or more different elements, 46

concentrated [KAHN-sun-trayt-ed] solution: strong solution, 118

condensation [kahn-dun-SAY-shun]:   change of a gas to a liquid, 138

conduction [kun-DUK-shun]:   the way heat moves through solids, 16

conductors: substances that conduct heat easily, 16

contract: make smaller, 8

convection [kuhn-VEK-shun]:   way heat moves through liquids and gases, 22

decomposition [dee-kahm-puh-ZISH-un]:   breakdown of a substance into simpler substances, 210

degree: unit used to measure temperature, 34

dilute: [di-LEWT] solution: weak solution, 118

dissolve: to cause to go into solution; to become liquid, 82, 106

distillation [dis-tuh-LAY-shun]:   process of evaporating a liquid and then condensing the gas back into a liquid, 138

electrolysis [i-lek-TRAHL-uh-sis]:   decomposition of a substance by means of electricity, 210

electrolyte [i-LEK-truh-lyt]:   substance that conducts an electric current when it is dissolved in water, 162

emulsion [i-MUL-shun]:   suspension of two liquids, 90

evaporate [i-VAP-uh-rayt]:   change from a liquid to a gas, 82

evaporation [i-vap-uh-RAY-shun]:   change of a liquid to a gas at the surface of the liquid, 138

expand: make larger, 8

Fahrenheit [FER-un-hyt]:   temperature scale, 40

filtration [fil-TRAY-shun]:   separation of particles in a suspension by passing it through paper or other substances, 98

formula mass: sum of the mass numbers of all atoms in a molecule, 184

formula unit: two or more atoms linked together by transferring electrons, but otherwise similar to a molecule, 46

friction: force that opposes the motion of an object, 2

heat: form of energy in moving particles of matter, 2

homogeneous [hoh-muh-JEE-nee-us]:   uniform; the same all the way through, 112

indicator [IN-duh-kayt-ur]:   substance that changes color in acids and bases, 144

inert gases: elements which have complete outer electron shells, gases which rarely react with other elements, 63 insulators: substances that do not conduct heat easily, 16

ion [I-un]: charged particle, 162

Law of Conservation of Matter: scientific statement that says that a chemical reaction does not destroy or create matter, 196

lend: to let someone use something that belongs to you, 58

mixture: two or more substances that are physically combined, 74

molecule [MAHL-uh-kyool]: the smallest part of a compound that has all the properties of that compound, two or more atoms linked together, 46

neutral: neither acidic nor basic, 156

neutralization [new-truh-li-ZAY-shun]: reaction between an acid and a base to produce a salt and water, 156

noble gases: inert gases, 63

oxidation [ahk-suh-DAY-shun]: linkup of oxygen with another substance; a loss of electrons, 222

oxidation numbers: the number of electrons an atom can lend or borrow, 168

phenolphthalein [fee-nohl-THAL-een]: an indicator that turns a deep pink color when a base is added, 150

physical change: a change in matter that does not produce any new products or substances, 66, 190

polyatomic [PAHL-i-uh-tahm-ik] ion: group of atoms that acts as a single atom, 176

polyvalent {pahl-i-VAY-lunt]: having more than one oxidation number, 180

product: a substance that is produced in a chemical reaction (change), 190

properties: [PROP-ur-tees]: characteristics used to describe a substance, 112

radiation [ray-dee-AY-shun]: the way heat moves through empty space, 28

reactant: substance that takes part in a chemical reaction (change), 190

reduction [ri-DUK-shun]: separation of oxygen from a substance; a gain of electrons, 222

reflect: bounce off, 28

replacement reaction: reaction in which one kind of matter replaces another kind, 216

saturated [SACH-uh-rayt-id] solution: solution containing all the solute it can hold at a given temperature, 118

shells: energy levels in which electrons are arranged around the nucleus, 58

solute [SAHL-yoot]: substance that is dissolved in a solvent, 106

solution: mixture in which one substance is evenly mixed with another substance, 106

solvent: substance in which a solute dissolves, 106

stable: is not likely to change, prefers to stay the way it is, 58

subscript: number written to the lower right of a chemical symbol, 176

suspension [suh-SPEN-shun]: cloudy mixture of two or more substances that settle on standing, 90

synthesis [SIN-thuh-sis] reaction: combining of several substances to form a more complicated substance, 204

temperature: measure of how hot or cold something is, 34

thermometer: instrument to measure temperature, 34

transparent [trans-PER-unt]: material that transmits light easily, 112

Tyndall effect: scattering of a light beam by particles in a colloid, 93